For more information write:

Ecotone Publishing
721 NW Ninth Avenue, Suite 195
Portland, OR 97209

Author: Mary Adam Thomas
Book Design: softfirm
Edited by: Fred McLennan, Liz Fetchin and Natalie Bowman
Primary Photography by: Denmarsh Photography Inc.

Library of Congress Control Number: 2013930977
Library of Congress Cataloging-in Publication Data

ISBN 978-0-9826902-1-5

1. ARCHITECTURE   2. ENVIRONMENT   3. PHILOSOPHY

First Edition

Printed in Canada on Reincarnation Matte paper — one hundred percent recycled content, processed chlorine free, using vegetable-based ink.

BUILDING IN BLOOM

The Making of the Center for Sustainable Landscapes
at Phipps Conservatory and Botanical Gardens

LIVING
BUILDING
CHALLENGE

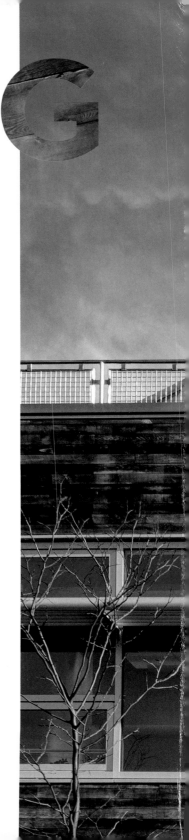

TABLE OF
CONTENTS

FOREWORD

"Imagine a building as elegant and efficient as a flower."

When I first heard those words, I knew Phipps was the perfect place to create that building; it represented a completely new way of thinking. I remember meeting Jason McLennan at Greenbuild in November of 2006 and being taken with his revolutionary vision. The Living Building Challenge™ puts it all together: energy, water, site, health, materials, equity, performance and, most notably, beauty. Beauty is often left out of the discussion. At Phipps, we are all about beauty, and we strive to show people that sustainable buildings and lifestyles can be just as appealing, if not more so, than conventional ones. Two months after I met Jason, our board accepted the challenge, and we were off.

It has been quite a journey. When we started our master planning back in 1999, we had no idea we would end up where we are today. At that time, we were not focused on green buildings; in fact, the green building movement was just getting started. Now that the Center for Sustainable Landscapes (CSL), the most progressive of our green building projects, is complete, we see how each step of the way has brought us closer to connecting with nature and thinking in systems, which is how nature works. This is important, because the more we learned, the more we

realized that many of the environmental issues we face today are a result of our disconnect from nature and our expectation that we will conquer it and bend it to our will. That will never happen; we are an inextricable part of nature.

We spend nearly 80 percent of our lives in buildings that are typically designed to isolate us from the environment, and, when we do go outside, we tend to think of nature as some distant place to visit, perhaps on a vacation. Yet the natural world is around us everywhere, every day, waiting for us to notice, experience and engage. The more we connect to the unique natural spaces we inhabit and integrate ourselves into natural cycles, the more attuned we become to valuing the environment and looking for better ways to live in harmony with it.

That is what first attracted me to the idea of taking the Living Building Challenge. In addition to practical Imperatives like net-zero energy and net-zero water, it is about relationships and has at its core an aspiration to restore a healthy connection with nature and celebrate beauty. In this way, it provides great opportunities to engage in biophillic design and embrace the landscape as a key and vital component of performance.

Taking the Challenge is transformational. What was most exciting to me was to see how the process of greening our buildings and operations completely changed the culture and image of Phipps. The enthusiasm with which our staff engaged in the process and embraced sustainability surpassed our expectations. Our board never wavered from doing the right thing and was so impassioned with our green evolution that they changed our mission statement to include sustainability as a core function of who we are and what we do. The community also supported this project, starting with major funders in our foundation community.

As we began to pull plans for the CSL together, we realized that this building shouldn't be just about Phipps, but rather celebrate all of the great talent we have in our region. Our friends, designers, consultants and contractors, almost all of whom are from Pittsburgh and Pennsylvania, take great pride in the CSL, which could not have come about without their interest and dedication. To all of them, we say thank you.

We are also grateful for the efforts of our staff, board, volunteers and friends at Carnegie Mellon University, the University of Pittsburgh and the Green Building Alliance. Their commitment doesn't end with the opening, because from good partnerships sprout many new opportunities. We are pleased to offer our building to our local universities and the National Energy

Technology Laboratory to monitor and study so that future buildings can be designed to be even more efficient than what we were able to achieve. For us, the CSL is not an endpoint, but rather a new beginning and a fresh opportunity to continue to learn and develop a whole new series of programs and relationships.

We see the connection between people, plants, health, planet and beauty in everything we do. This inspires us to align our actions with our values. As we adjust to a new way of thinking about how we work in the built environment, we will look for every opportunity to fulfill what we see as the ultimate goal of a Living Building: to continue to learn and help people reestablish their connection to nature.

As I look back to when we first contemplated accepting the Challenge, I am not surprised that there never was a debate over costs or whether or not we should have done this. I think that is because when your mission, vision and values encourage you to imagine and build a future world worth living in, you will find the will and the way to do it.

RICHARD V. PIACENTINI
Executive Director,
Phipps Conservatory and Botanical Gardens

3

ACKNOWLEDGEMENTS

I am enormously grateful to Jason F. McLennan for inviting me into the world of Living Buildings back in 2006 and entrusting me since that time with some of its stories. I am among a planetful of people who benefit from Jason's ideas. Working with him has made me a better writer and a more informed environmental advocate.

Thanks to Richard V. Piacentini for his vision, Liz Fetchin for her grace, and the collective Phipps and CSL teams for having the courage and determination to create this astonishing building. I am honored to be the one asked to summarize their revolutionary accomplishment.

My sincere appreciation to Michael Berrisford at Ecotone Publishing, who always finds a way to make me feel as if I'm right on track. To Ecotone's Fred McLennan and Phipps' Natalie Bowman for their thorough editing, which helped make this book infinitely more readable. To Pittsburgh-based architecture photographer Alexander Denmarsh and his colleague Elliott Cramer, for their beautiful images capturing the CSL as it came to life. And to softfirm's Erin Gehle and Johanna Björk, who wrapped everything in a beautifully designed bow.

Finally, to Kevin, Mackenzie and Reed, whose love and encouragement keep me living, keep me building and keep me challenged — in all the best ways — every single day.

MARY ADAM THOMAS
2013

AUTHOR PROFILE

Mary Adam Thomas is an independent writer who plays with words through her business, Thomas Communications. She is the collaborative author of Jason F. McLennan's collection of essays, *Zugunruhe: The Inner Migration to Profound Environmental Change* and of *The Web-Savvy Patient: An Insider's Guide to Navigating the Internet When Facing Medical Crisis* by Andrew Schorr. In addition, Mary contributed the introduction to McLennan's follow-up essay collection, *Transformational Thought: Radical Ideas to Remake the Built Environment.* Her broad portfolio of written work includes essays and editorial pieces that have appeared in a wide variety of print and online publications catering to consumer and professional audiences. Mary lives in the Seattle area with her husband and their two children.

PART I

Fertile Soil

A Rich History,
a Sustainable Mission

Part I: **FERTILE SOIL**

ENTERING A GREEN WORLD

Phipps Conservatory and Botanical Gardens makes a striking impression from the outside. The elegant glass dome at its entrance is framed by the majestic profile of its distinctly Victorian greenhouse. As one begins to circle the campus perimeter, a dramatic modern structure comes into view, with high-climbing glass walls that reflect the patterns of the clouds. Toward the rear of the property sits a three-level building nestled against the hillside it shares with a wind turbine and a field of photovoltaic solar panels. Walkways and gardens tie one structure to another, connecting past with future and nature with the built environment. The Phipps campus sits proudly amid the gentle slopes of Pittsburgh's Schenley Park, a public sanctuary originally granted to the community in 1889.

Once inside, visitors begin to take in all that is Phipps. After proceeding past the gift shop, café and ticket booth, guests enter the Palm Court — the facility's official gateway to its many interior display rooms. The historic space can only be described as lush, with natural growth at all heights: from the sprawling groundcover that lines the bluestone walkway to the tall palms reaching toward the court's glassy ceiling. The air is clean, the breezes gentle, the sounds soothing and the colors vivid.

Phipps is where nature is most celebrated in Pittsburgh. It does more than just offer a peaceful escape from urban chaos. It has a more profound effect on those who stroll its grounds: it reminds us that we have a collective responsibility to respect and restore the strength of our natural surroundings. Phipps houses flowers and plants, but it stands as a symbol of progress for the greater environmental movement.

The Conservatory has worked hard to earn its international leadership position among environmentally responsible public gardens. Its mission has adapted as worldviews have changed over the course of its long history. When Phipps first opened its doors a century ago, humans considered nature to be a separate commodity — something that could be put into a box and observed from a distance. Phipps and facilities like it offered almost zoo-like settings where people could view nature on display with detachment. Today, our more sophisticated understanding of the natural world gives us an appropriate degree of humility. We know enough about the complex interdependencies between our species and the planet to take some responsibility for the effects of our actions. Specifically, we are beginning to grasp that our built environment should be part of, not distinct from, our natural environment. Inside and out, Phipps has come a long way since its 19th-century infancy.

8

THE CONSERVATORY TAKES SHAPE

Henry W. Phipps, Jr. commissioned Phipps Conservatory in the early 1890s as a gift to the City of Pittsburgh after making his fortune in the local steel and real estate industries. Workers broke ground in 1892 and noted greenhouse builder Lord & Burnham led design and construction. The first plants and flowers showcased in the greenhouse were shipped from Chicago, where they had been on display at the 1893 World's Columbian Exposition.

Henry W. Phipps, Jr.

On the occasion of its centennial anniversary in 1993, Phipps converted from a public to a private nonprofit entity. Management of the organization signed a new 100-year lease with the city and started making plans for its second century of service. During the mid-1990s, the board of trustees made several key strategic decisions:

- They changed the name to Phipps Conservatory and Botanical Gardens to reflect the facility's expanding scope.

- They hired Richard V. Piacentini as the new executive director. With advanced degrees in both botany and business, as well as a personal passion for environmentalism, he was the ideal candidate to lead the organization into the next century.

- They made a sweeping commitment to sustainability in all aspects of the facility's operations.

A Phipps promotional postcard, circa 1890s.

Many of Phipps' plants and flowers were displayed on waist-high benches during the early 20th century.

An elaborate Fall Flower Show.

10

THE MISSION EVOLVES AND ADAPTS

The original mission of Phipps Conservatory reflected an unfortunate reality for most late 19th-century Pittsburgh citizens: working conditions in this industrial city could be grueling, living conditions could be gritty, and economic conditions could be arduous. Henry Phipps' original vision for the property was to create an amenity that would offer the masses a refuge from the rigors of daily life. He wanted to give them an escape from hardships, a place whose visual beauty was as dramatic as its restorative properties. At the greenhouse, the plants were exotic and the air was cleaner. The Conservatory set out to harness the power of nature as a way of benefitting the whole person.

Victorian-era sensibilities gave humanity a sense of power over nature. In the Industrial Age, the assumption was that humans could and should conquer the natural environment. Phipps Conservatory set out to embody that cultural ideal. Plants were brought to Pittsburgh from all over the world and displayed in a grand man-made facility. Although the underlying intention was to offer visitors a better understanding of botany, the Phipps model required that tropical plants be imported to Pittsburgh's temperate climate and housed in a single-pane glass structure. Looking at this upside-down form of environmentalism through a modern lens reveals its flaws, but Henry Phipps and his contemporaries did not have the depth of understanding that we do today. They believed resources to be endless and climate forces to be stable. Energy was theirs to consume in their quest to bring nature to the people.

Phipps Conservatory and Botanical Gardens' present-day mission (introduced in 2007) expands on the original in profound ways, setting a dramatic and proactive tone with the careful reworking of just a few words. It establishes the organization's unequivocal commitment to sustainability, biodiversity and research, and clearly conveys Phipps' interest in taking a leadership role in the local and global environmental movements. It demonstrates how celebrating nature can be more than an exercise in aesthetics; it can alter the fundamental ways in which we live.

These days, Phipps takes a more holistic approach to its work. In the 21st century, it has reinvented itself not only as one of the greenest public gardens in the world, but also as an all-around leader in teaching environmental awareness. At all levels of the organization, the Conservatory now takes the opportunity to pursue and promote sustainability. In recent years, these green efforts have centered on initiatives that came about through a three-phase expansion of its campus.

WE SHALL ENDEAVOR TO ERECT SOMETHING THAT WILL PROVE A SOURCE OF INSTRUCTION AS WELL AS PLEASURE TO THE PEOPLE.

FIRST MISSION OF PHIPPS CONSERVATORY
From a letter written by Henry Phipps to Pittsburgh Mayor H.I. Gourley, 1891

TO INSPIRE AND EDUCATE ALL WITH THE BEAUTY AND IMPORTANCE OF PLANTS; TO ADVANCE SUSTAINABILITY AND PROMOTE HUMAN AND ENVIRONMENTAL WELL-BEING THROUGH ACTION AND RESEARCH; AND TO CELEBRATE ITS HISTORIC GLASSHOUSE.

MISSION OF PHIPPS CONSERVATORY AND BOTANICAL GARDENS

Henry Phipps set out to create a natural, rejuvenating sanctuary for Pittsburgh's citizenry.

ENVISIONING THE GREENEST OF GARDENS

In 2000, Phipps launched a $36.6 million capital campaign to fund its ambitious renovation and expansion plan. The new campus would accommodate the facility's growing inventory and rising attendance while providing a physical space that would reflect its environmental commitment and offer improved visitor amenities. Richard V. Piacentini and members of the board of trustees appealed to local, regional and national donors interested in supporting this audacious but exciting trio of projects. The response was overwhelmingly positive and Phipps, already recognized as a leader in horticulture, was soon on its way to turning its campus into a sustainable design showcase.

PHASE I: NEW WELCOME CENTER

Phipps broke ground in October 2003 for its new main entrance, which would also house a gift shop and café. Designed by architects at Pittsburgh-based IKM, Inc. to complement the aesthetics of the Conservatory's original Lord & Burnham architecture, the new 12,465-square-foot space incorporates enough green elements to achieve Leadership in Energy and Environmental Design® (LEED) Silver certification. The building sits partly underground, which naturally helps insulate it from extreme temperatures. Heating pipes beneath the walkway channel waste heat from steam condensate to warm the sidewalks,

eliminating the need for gas-powered snow-clearing machines or toxic de-icing chemicals. The glass dome and insulated wall of windows serve decorative and energy-efficient functions, as they allow natural light to bathe the interior. A green roof surrounding the dome provides a heat sink, further enhancing the efficiency of the building's climate control systems. When it opened in 2005, Phipps' Welcome Center was the first LEED-certified visitor center in a public garden and Café Phipps has since earned a prestigious Green Restaurant Certified® three-star rating and a national sustainability award from the Hobart Center for Foodservice Sustainability.

PHASE II: TROPICAL FOREST CONSERVATORY AND PRODUCTION GREENHOUSES

In 2006, Phipps made history again when it opened the impressive 12,000-square-foot Tropical Forest Conservatory and the adjacent 36,000-square-foot Production Greenhouse facility. Although plans for these structures incorporated state-of-the-art green features and systems, Piacentini and his team chose not to pursue LEED certification at the time — primarily because they were led to believe that the all-glass buildings would never meet the minimum energy requirements for attaining it. Instead, they decided to include as many green strategies as possible, but not work toward any specified set of certification rules. As construction proceeded, however, Piacentini realized that not having a stated green building standard for which to strive meant that the project tended to veer off the green track too easily. So he assigned himself the job of keeping Phase II well within the sustainable realm by incorporating as many built-in efficiencies as possible. In fact, working closely with the architecture/construction/engineering team, he pushed through several of the ideas that would prove to be the buildings' greenest features:

earth tubes for passive cooling, open-roof technology to eliminate the "greenhouse effect," thermal massing in the walls to collect solar energy by day and warm the interior by night, the world's first in-conservatory fuel cell for cleaner electricity, selective use of insulated glass, a two-stage shading system that would double as an energy blanket, and more. Each separate function contributed to the efficiency of the larger system. The result is the most energy-efficient conservatory in the world. In 2012, the Production Greenhouses earned LEED for Existing Buildings: Operations & Maintenance (LEED EBOM) Platinum certification, which is awarded to structures demonstrating best operational practices and performance efficiencies.

PHASE III: CENTER FOR SUSTAINABLE LANDSCAPES

In the third and final phase of the expansion plan, Phipps would create a new building to house its education, research and administration operations. Plans for the Center for Sustainable Landscapes (CSL) were drawn up in 2003 along with the plans for the expansion's first two phases. Although Phipps initially opted not to seek LEED certification (or any other official

stamp of green approval), the CSL was designed to be more energy efficient than a conventional building. However, by the time Phase II construction was under way, funds for Phase III had become scarce. In the early 2000s, the price of concrete and steel had escalated dramatically and had taxed the overall $36.6 million budget. As Phase II neared completion, Phipps had to make an important decision: It could value engineer all of the green features out of Phase II so that Phase III could proceed, or keep the green features in Phase II and put off Phase III to some later date. Standing firm on his and Phipps' stated goal to remain committed to sustainability in all aspects of the organization, Piacentini recommended that they postpone Phase III, and asked the board of trustees to decide how to proceed. Together, they agreed on the intrinsic and strategic value of these buildings, and decided to cover Phase II's extra costs by reallocating much of Phase III's budget. By late 2006, plans for the CSL were on hold pending the launch of a new fundraising campaign scheduled for several years hence. At this time, Piacentini predicted that when he and the board eventually revisited the project, they would likely need to abandon the building's existing architectural drawings and start fresh with a better, greener design.

13

"We think of Phipps as being a place of beauty and inspiration. Underneath that, we think of it as a place where we can help people discover more sustainable, more environmentally friendly, more harmonious ways to interact with the natural world. Phipps really helps connect the dots between people, plants, biodiversity, health, the environment, food — even green buildings and green operations. We've discovered in our journey that all these things are interrelated. Whatever happens with one affects everything else."

RICHARD V. PIACENTINI
Phipps Conservatory and
Botanical Gardens

14

15

A GAME-CHANGING MEETING

Shortly before the opening of the Tropical Forest Conservatory in late 2006, Piacentini traveled to Denver to attend the Greenbuild® International Conference and Expo. Operated by the U.S. Green Building Council, which oversees LEED certification, this annual industry event draws professionals from a variety of disciplines who share a commitment to and passion for sustainable design. Piacentini went as a lay person interested in the field as well as a newly experienced green project owner. He hoped to share the story of Phipps' latest accomplishments and expand on his knowledge of sustainability.

Chatting with a fellow Greenbuild attendee on the second day of the conference, Piacentini summarized Phipps' recent green building achievements. He proudly described the campus' completed buildings from Phases I and II, and then outlined the key features he hoped to incorporate into the CSL when Phase III was back on the drawing board. He described the way the building would fulfill its own energy and water needs, and would be designed according to a whole-system approach. The attendee explained to Piacentini that the building he envisioned would achieve many of the goals of the Living Building Challenge™ — a far-reaching green building concept officially introduced at Greenbuild the previous night by its author, Jason F. McLennan, CEO of the Cascadia Green Building Council and the International Living Future Institute.

Intrigued, Piacentini went in search of McLennan. When they met, the two men shared their stories: Piacentini about Phipps' sustainable mission and McLennan about the Living Building Challenge — a progressive program calling for buildings to operate as efficiently and beautifully as a flower or plant. They agreed that Phipps was primed for the Challenge. After all, the Tropical Forest Conservatory and Production Greenhouses already met many deep green building standards; there was no reason not to go for the deepest of them all with the CSL.

Richard V. Piacentini (left) and
Jason F. McLennan (right) tour
the CSL construction site.

"Richard is very much an early adopter. With him, it's always about 'Why aren't we doing this already?' He's very progressive in terms of trying new things. He's already extremely green, but he wants to be even greener."

MARC MONDOR
evolveEA

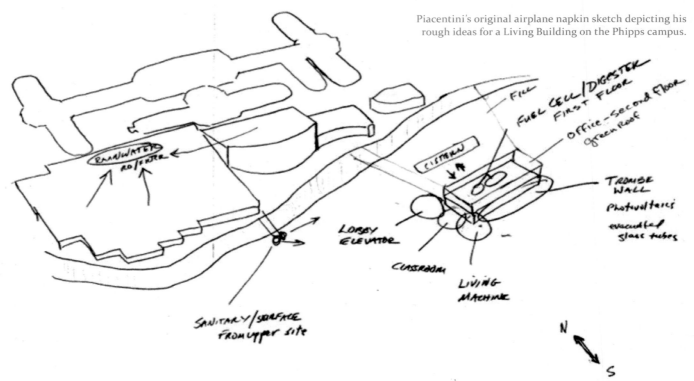

Piacentini's original airplane napkin sketch depicting his rough ideas for a Living Building on the Phipps campus.

A NEW DIRECTION

> "Right after we opened the Tropical Forest Conservatory, a number of donors asked what was next. When they heard about the Living Building idea, they urged us not to wait, to do this now. The board voted to proceed with the Living Building Challenge a few weeks later. From the beginning, we knew it was important for us to make this about community, not just about Phipps."
>
> **RICHARD V. PIACENTINI**
> Phipps Conservatory and Botanical Gardens

On his flight home from Denver, Piacentini sketched on a napkin his updated vision for the CSL — now as a self-sustaining Living Building. The new scheme called for a structure that required no outside water or energy, was created using local materials and talent, and was restorative to its site and occupants.

Back in Pittsburgh, he reported the details of his trip to the Phipps board. They agreed that shifting gears and redesigning the CSL as a Living Building was a radical idea. Fundraising was not scheduled to begin again for Phase III for at least another three years, so the idea was put on hold, as Phipps wanted to give donors a much-deserved rest. Still, the idea began to build its own momentum, partly because of the increasing amount of interest people from all over the globe were taking in Phipps and its deeply green building innovations.

Immediately following the successful opening of the Phase II facilities on December 7, 2006, donors wanted to know what was to come next. When they heard about Phipps' plans for a Living Building, they made it clear that the organization should not wait and expressed their interest in supporting the next transformative step at one of the world's greenest public gardens.

Buoyed by community interest, the board of trustees formally voted in January 2007 to accept the Living Building Challenge for the third and final phase of Phipps' expansion. Piacentini had his napkin sketch professionally rendered, using the conceptual drawing as the primary graphic in promotional materials. Fundraising for the CSL — a proposed Living Building — began in earnest that month, as did Phipps' most ambitious project in its 114-year history.

17

Part I: FERTILE SOIL

THE LIVING BUILDING CHALLENGE™

Phipps accepted version 1.3 of the Living Building Challenge, which had been updated several times from the original version 1.0 introduced in 2006. The Living Building Challenge version 1.3 contains 16 Imperatives categorized within six performance area Petals. Qualifying projects fall into one of four types: renovation, landscape or infrastructure, building, or neighborhood. On the following page is a brief summary of the Challenge. Full text of the Living Building Challenge version 1.3 may be viewed and downloaded on the International Living Future Institute website: **www.living-future.org**.

18

Two rules govern the standard:

1. All elements of the Living Building Challenge are mandatory. Many of the requirements have temporary exceptions to acknowledge current market limitations. These are listed in the footnotes of each section. Exceptions will be modified or removed as the market changes.

2. Living Building designation is based on actual, rather than modeled or anticipated, performance. Therefore, buildings must be operational for at least 12 consecutive months prior to evaluation.

SITE PETAL

Restoring a healthy coexistence with nature

Imperative 1   Responsible Site Selection
Imperative 2   Limits to Growth
Imperative 3   Habitat Exchange

WATER PETAL

Creating water-independent sites, buildings and communities

Imperative 10   Net-Zero Water
Imperative 11   Sustainable Water Discharge

ENERGY PETAL

Relying only on current solar income

Imperative 4   Net-Zero Energy

INDOOR QUALITY PETAL

Maximizing physical and psychological health and well-being

Imperative 12   Civilized Environment
Imperative 13   Healthy Air: Source Control
Imperative 14   Healthy Air: Ventilation

MATERIALS PETAL

Endorsing products and processes that are safe for all species through time

Imperative 5   Red List
Imperative 6   Construction Carbon Footprint
Imperative 7   Responsible Industry
Imperative 8   Appropriate Materials/ Services Radius
Imperative 9   Leadership in Construction Waste

BEAUTY AND INSPIRATION PETAL

Celebrating design that creates transformative change

Imperative 15   Beauty and Spirit
Imperative 16   Inspiration and Education

PART II

Strong Seeds

The Team, the Process
and the Plan

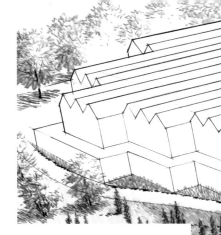

The implementation of this standard requires leading-edge technical knowledge, an integrated design approach, and design and construction teams well-versed in advanced practices related to green building.

FROM THE LIVING BUILDING CHALLENGE VERSION 1.3

REGISTERING THE PROJECT

Phipps Conservatory and Botanical Gardens initiated its relationship with the International Living Future Institute (ILFI) in early 2007 by submitting a brief description of its proposed Living Building:

The new facility, called the Center for Sustainable Landscapes (CSL), is to be located on Phipps' existing campus. The original conservatory was built in 1893 and the historic site includes a series of spectacular indoor and outdoor gardens. The silver LEED certified Welcome Center that opened in 2005 was the first LEED certified visitor center in a Public Garden. The Tropical Forest Conservatory, December 2006, is the most energy efficient conservatory in the world. Phipps' mission is to inspire and educate visitors with the beauty and importance of plants; to advance sustainability and worldwide biodiversity through action and research and to celebrate its historic glasshouse.

The purpose of this facility will be to provide classroom education for both young and old and house a research and outreach program aimed at supporting regional efforts that encourage smart practices in sustainable landscape design, construction and management.

The CSL was only the fifth project to register for Living Building Challenge certification. As such, the CSL and the Challenge evolved and adapted simultaneously. Just as the building took shape, so too did the standard it was designed to achieve.

A Living Building Challenge project must document consistent performance figures over a minimum of 12 consecutive months of operations and full-time occupancy. Only then is it eligible to be evaluated by an independent third-party auditor who determines whether or not it has met all of the requirements. If it has, it earns full Living Building Challenge certification through ILFI.

22

An architectural rendering of the CSL (center), rooftop photovoltaic arrays (right) and Phipps' upper campus (above).

"Phipps' project was one of the earliest registered for the Living Building Challenge. Since they were one of the first to adopt the program, we could give and get real feedback about where the standard might be tweaked. Because of the many ways they let us into their world, we learned a lot about how the Challenge could evolve to adapt to the realities of these projects."

EDEN BRUKMAN
International Living
Future Institute

23

Part II: STRONG SEEDS

L. Christian Minnerly (left) and his colleagues at The Design Alliance Architects were chosen to lead the CSL project in part because they made it clear to Phipps Executive Director Richard V. Piacentini (right) that they were interested in collaboration.

"Richard Piacentini is such an innovator and he's always looking for the next cutting-edge strategy — especially one that links to the mission of the Conservatory. When he first came to Pittsburgh, he immediately reached out to as many local players as he could to find out who were the innovators, what were the technologies, what were the strategies."

VIVIAN LOFTNESS
Carnegie Mellon University
School of Architecture

AN ELITE TEAM

With a new vision firmly in place for the CSL, Piacentini set out to assemble the team that would help turn this green dream into reality. He sought professionals and academics experienced in sustainable design and construction who were as intrigued as he was by the idea of pushing the envelope within the built environment. This project would take them into uncharted territory, so everyone involved needed to embrace the unknown. In addition, Piacentini knew that the key to creating the best team was finding individuals who would welcome and benefit from a collaborative approach. He had initiated multiple design and construction changes to "green up" the Tropical Forest Conservatory and Production Greenhouses as they were being built, and was fortunate to work with professionals who supported his requests. But he was aware that mid-stream changes were not ideal, even on traditionally built projects. His goal for the CSL was to finalize the building's

master plan before any architectural drawings were completed or any ground was broken.

To get things started, Piacentini contacted two of the country's most prestigious architecture and engineering schools, both of which happen to be located right in Pittsburgh. He consulted faculty at the Center for Building Performance and Diagnostics at Carnegie Mellon University and at the Mascaro Center for Sustainable Innovation at the University of Pittsburgh. He also reached out to the Green Building Alliance, Pittsburgh's U.S. Green Building Council affiliate, to gauge their interest in getting involved. Everyone enthusiastically agreed to support Phipps in its efforts.

In April 2007, Piacentini attended Living Future, the first annual conference sponsored by the Cascadia Green Building Council and the International Living Future Institute, both run by Jason F. McLennan. Piacentini sat in on

24

The design, engineering, construction and environmental professionals who came together to lend their expertise to the CSL project have been referred to as Pittsburgh's "green dream team."

a session about facilitated integrated design, a method used on an increasing number of green projects — and the required system of the Living Building Challenge. He returned to Pittsburgh and asked his team to write into the project's request for proposal (RFP) that interested parties must be willing to design and build the CSL using facilitated integrated design as the operating approach, as he was convinced that this was the only way one could build a high-performance green building.

Piacentini was committed to using as many Pittsburgh-based firms as possible in order to showcase the green talent already present in western Pennsylvania. Phipps hired Pittsburgh consulting group evolveEA to help craft the RFP, develop a short list of design teams and review all applicants. They interviewed five teams, each led by an architect who brought his or her own hand-picked roster of engineers

and other specialists. The fundamental idea was to choose discipline leaders who would understand how their decisions would affect all other systems operating inside and outside of the building. In short, they wanted to create what integrated design facilitator John Boecker referred to as a "composite master builder."

After careful review, Phipps selected Pittsburgh-based The Design Alliance Architects to lead the CSL design-build effort, with L. Christian ("Chris") Minnerly serving as chief architect. Minnerly stood out not only because he and his extended team demonstrated skill and experience, but also because he expressed genuine interest in learning all that the Living Building Challenge and the CSL could teach him. He and his colleagues wanted to deepen their professional knowledge by contributing their expertise to this revolutionary local endeavor. They were humbled, not hindered, by the opportunity to collaborate.

"The selection process was based on what we thought of the architect, but also what we thought of the rest of the team. We asked teams how they thought they fit with us and how they would operate within an integrated design approach. The way they came across in the interviews was key; some architects showed up with preliminary design ideas and some of their consultants gave us the sense that they were waiting for the architects to give them the plans before they'd put their piece in. But that wasn't what we wanted. Chris Minnerly came across as someone who was really easygoing, interested in collaboration and open to integrated design."

RICHARD V. PIACENTINI
Phipps Conservatory and Botanical Gardens

25

AIMING FOR DISTINCTLY GREEN TARGETS

By fall 2007, the CSL had a design team in place and facilitators were ready to initiate the integrated design process. Even before the group gathered for the first time, it was important for Phipps to clearly define the project's three green goals:

1. **Living Building Challenge certification** — issued by the International Living Future Institute only after 12 months of full occupancy and operation, and based on quantifiable performance measures.

2. **Leadership in Energy and Environmental Design® (LEED) Platinum certification** — the highest possible sustainable design rating from the U.S. Green Building Council.

3. **Sustainable Sites Initiative™ (SITES™) certification for landscapes** — issued by the American Society of Landscape Architects, the Lady Bird Johnson Wildflower Center at the University of Texas at Austin, and the United States Botanic Garden. (SITES guidelines had not yet been released when the CSL design team began its work, but lead landscape architect José Almiñana was on the SITES steering committee, so he helped design the landscape to anticipated SITES standards. The CSL was accepted as a SITES pilot project in spring 2010.)

"As an exercise, we looked into the etymology of various words. The verb 'to integrate' actually means 'to unify or make whole' and 'whole' means 'uninjured.' Then we got to the verb 'to heal' which is 'to make whole.' So the conclusion is that integrating is healing."

JOHN BOECKER
7Group

26

INTEGRATED DESIGN DEFINED

The purpose of integrated design is to gather people from disparate disciplines and focus their collective efforts toward a single goal: creating a project that marries high performance with elegant expression. In the case of the CSL, the purpose was to plan a building that generated its own energy, provided its own water, used environmentally responsible materials, had appropriate impact on its surroundings, enhanced the health of its occupants, and inspired its visitors.

As one of the world's first structures to pursue Living Building status, the CSL had no precedent. The architect, engineers, landscape designers and contractor would need to create one-of-a-kind building systems for this first-of-its-kind structure. Each discipline had to inform all others, so every specialist needed to weigh in on all major decisions. The facilitator's job was to break down barriers among the various specialties while illuminating individual strategies that would benefit the whole — in other words, to move people from fragmented to more holistic ways of thinking.

> *"Designing a Living Building is complicated enough; the logic of the integrated design process is well-suited to that."*
>
> **L. CHRISTIAN MINNERLY**
> The Design Alliance Architects

27

Design charrettes for the CSL brought together project participants from all disciplines. Architect L. Christian Minnerly, Phipps' Richard V. Piacentini and landscape architect José Almiñana (shown left to right at top left) were regularly in attendance.

"When an architect engages in this robust type of process, the building ends up almost drawing itself. We're not drawing something and then figuring out how to make it work; we're figuring out how to make everything work together first and the result emerges from that. It turns the normal design process inside out."

JOHN BOECKER
7Group

INTEGRATED DESIGN FOR THE CENTER FOR SUSTAINABLE LANDSCAPES

The first "all-hands" design charrette for the CSL took place on October 16, 2007 in Phipps' new Special Events Hall adjacent to the Tropical Forest Conservatory. John Boecker of the Pennsylvania consulting firm 7Group served as the facilitator for the meeting. He began by establishing the vision for the project and getting all players up to speed on the Living Building Challenge, LEED and SITES certification parameters, initially aligning everyone around goals rather than performance targets. Then he set the collaborative tone that would flow through the 14 subsequent charrettes, reminding participants that constraints were their friends and agenda creep was always welcome.

The integrated design roadmap guided the team toward its next steps, which Boecker referred to as "touchstones." Following each meeting, individuals researched and analyzed the systems that pertained to their areas of expertise. At the subsequent charrette, contributors compared notes and explored beneficial relationships among multiple systems. As meetings continued, the team honed more clearly onto specific systems and design goals. All participants left each meeting aligned around increasingly detailed plans. This ongoing exchange of ideas continued for months.

29

Estimated Annual Energy Costs

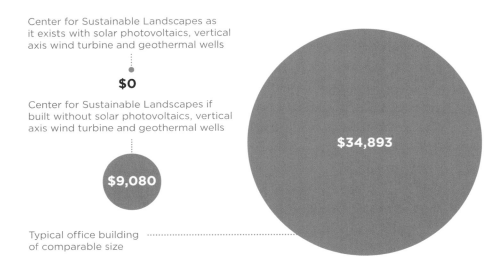

Center for Sustainable Landscapes as it exists with solar photovoltaics, vertical axis wind turbine and geothermal wells

$0

Center for Sustainable Landscapes if built without solar photovoltaics, vertical axis wind turbine and geothermal wells

$9,080

$34,893

Typical office building of comparable size

Expected Daily Water Consumption

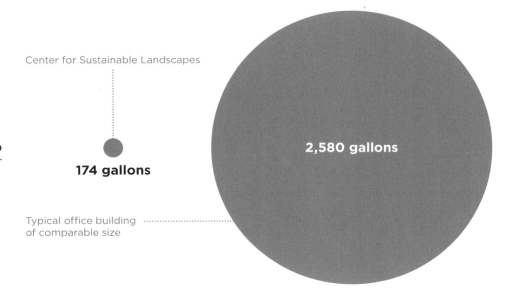

Center for Sustainable Landscapes

174 gallons

2,580 gallons

Typical office building of comparable size

"*Process is everything. This project had multiple all-day design charrettes, which is unheard of. But it paid off in so many ways. The people involved in the CSL all believed in what it could, should and would be. They made time to be at those meetings even when they had no time. They were enthralled by the possibilities; they felt they were part of something that would really make a difference.*"

AURORA L. SHARRARD
Green Building Alliance

31

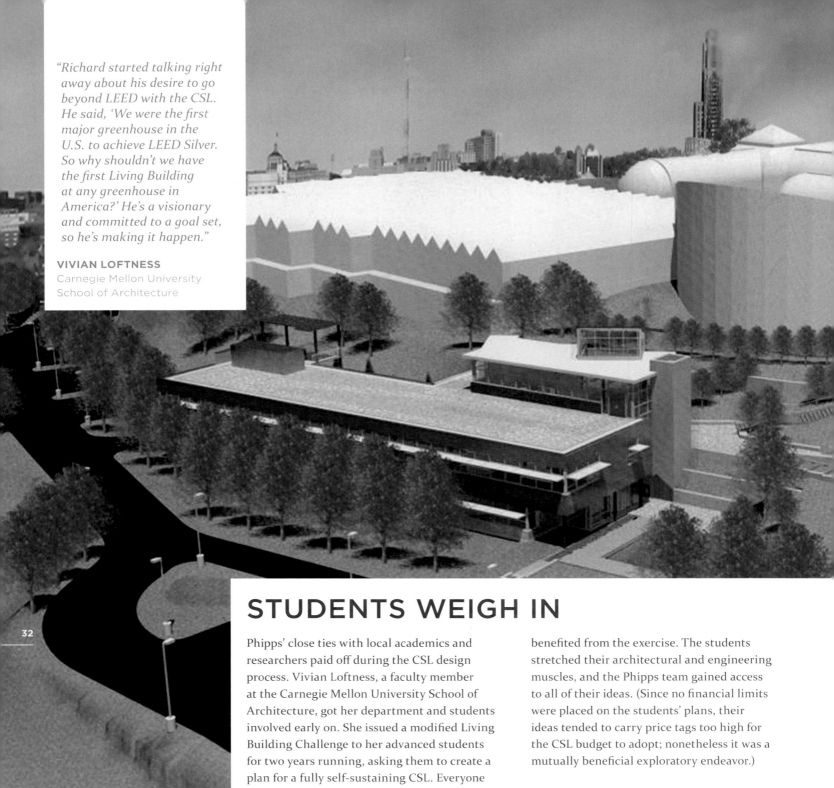

> "Richard started talking right away about his desire to go beyond LEED with the CSL. He said, 'We were the first major greenhouse in the U.S. to achieve LEED Silver. So why shouldn't we have the first Living Building at any greenhouse in America?' He's a visionary and committed to a goal set, so he's making it happen."
>
> **VIVIAN LOFTNESS**
> Carnegie Mellon University
> School of Architecture

STUDENTS WEIGH IN

Phipps' close ties with local academics and researchers paid off during the CSL design process. Vivian Loftness, a faculty member at the Carnegie Mellon University School of Architecture, got her department and students involved early on. She issued a modified Living Building Challenge to her advanced students for two years running, asking them to create a plan for a fully self-sustaining CSL. Everyone benefited from the exercise. The students stretched their architectural and engineering muscles, and the Phipps team gained access to all of their ideas. (Since no financial limits were placed on the students' plans, their ideas tended to carry price tags too high for the CSL budget to adopt; nonetheless it was a mutually beneficial exploratory endeavor.)

REFLECTION TIME

Reflection time was carefully incorporated into each design workshop. Facilitators paused at least once during each charrette and asked participants to ponder where the team was in the process and how much progress they were making. Piacentini and others representing Phipps as the owner of the project were specifically singled out, as their input was critical. The exercise gave people the opportunity to voice any concerns regarding the building's proposed design and systems, while providing a forum for general process-related feedback.

The team ended up altering the CSL's parking strategy as a result of reflection time. Given the multiple functions that the building would add to the Phipps operation, the reality was that it would bring more people — and more cars — to the campus. But the idea of building a parking lot to serve one of the world's greenest buildings ran counter to the project's mission. For many months, the team skirted the issue by assuming that visitors would seek green solutions on their own; they could use public transportation, ride bikes, or park elsewhere in Schenley Park. In short, the project team considered it a potentially unsolvable problem rather than an opportunity to develop new ways of thinking.

But in one of the final charrettes, Boecker asked for reflections. Two members of the group raised their hands simultaneously. Although they were reluctant to go against the green tide, they had jointly decided that the parking strategy — or lack thereof — was problematic. The building simply would not function well without adequate vehicular access. Wasn't there a way to come up with an approach that served the building, its occupants and its mission?

The rest of the team acknowledged the unfortunate truth of the matter and revisited the subject. Once again, they discussed and debated various possibilities, approaching the problem from new angles. (The most Challenge-friendly solution would have been to prohibit gas-powered vehicles from entering the campus, but it was an unrealistic expectation.) The group ultimately crafted a solution that they jointly agreed was workable within the confines of the project and the physical limitations of the site. A handful of parking spaces are now provided adjacent to the CSL and are reserved for people conducting business with staff at the building. All other vehicles park at the upper campus. Thanks to reflection time, the parking issue became a new action item that was reworked until the team landed on an improved plan. (For more on the parking solution implemented at the CSL, see page 59.)

An early rough study model of the CSL.

"Too often, university faculty and students aren't out in the field and don't have the opportunity to work with great organizations that are doing innovative things. With Phipps' proximity to our campus, we're fortunate to be able to work closely on projects like this that make a real difference."

STEPHEN LEE
Carnegie Mellon University School of Architecture

"Integration helps teams see a building and its site as an organism with systems that interact — not unlike the systems in the body. The ventilation is the respiratory system, electricity is the circulatory system, and controls are the nervous system. All of these systems operate in elegant concert with each other, with very little redundancy and waste. That's really the goal of an integrated process: to design a building that functions as an organism with a team that does so also."

JOHN BOECKER
7Group

CHECKING IN WITH THE INTERNATIONAL LIVING FUTURE INSTITUTE

From the first charrette, the team had questions about the Living Building Challenge beyond what was defined in the official text developed by the ILFI. As a result, the team decided early on in the process that one person should serve as the liaison between Phipps and the ILFI. Aurora Sharrard from the Green Building Alliance was the obvious choice.

Her organization is the local U.S. Green Building Council affiliate, she has a doctorate in civil/environmental engineering, is a certified LEED AP, and she has had previous professional interactions with ILFI Vice President Eden Brukman.

After accepting the liaison appointment, Sharrard became responsible for taking the team's questions to Brukman, who clarified program requirements and helped keep Phipps' plan in alignment with the Challenge. Since the CSL was one of the first registered projects, Brukman was extremely engaged in dialogue with the team. And, while the Challenge was well-defined in theory, Phipps' project helped shine light on how it behaved when put into practice. Needless to say, both organizations learned a lot as they went along.

> "We had lots of questions very early on because there were so many charrettes and so many strong minds thinking about this problem from the very beginning. We just wanted to align with the intent from the very beginning so we didn't hit surprises later on. We were concerned about making an early decision that would cost us certification at the end."

AURORA L. SHARRARD
Green Building Alliance

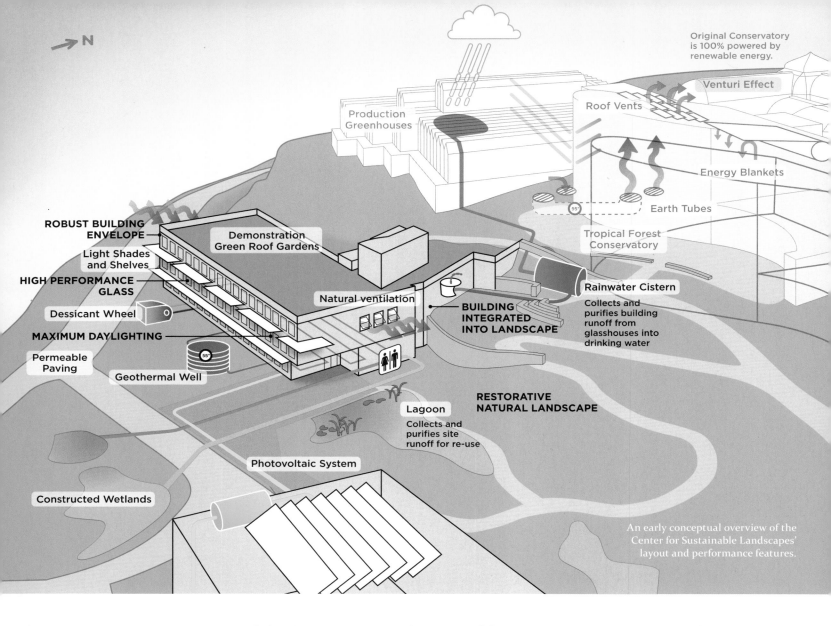

N

Venturi Effect

Production Greenhouses

Roof Vents

Energy Blankets

Earth Tubes

Tropical Forest Conservatory

ROBUST BUILDING ENVELOPE

Demonstration Green Roof Gardens

Light Shades and Shelves

HIGH PERFORMANCE GLASS

Dessicant Wheel

Natural ventilation

BUILDING INTEGRATED INTO LANDSCAPE

MAXIMUM DAYLIGHTING

Rainwater Cistern
Collects and purifies building runoff from glasshouses into drinking water

Permeable Paving

Geothermal Well

RESTORATIVE NATURAL LANDSCAPE

Lagoon
Collects and purifies site runoff for re-use

Photovoltaic System

Constructed Wetlands

An early conceptual overview of the Center for Sustainable Landscapes' layout and performance features.

36

"It's so important to carry the integrated design process into construction. Early on, as requests for information — or RFIs — came in from the subcontractors, one of the design team project managers served as gatekeeper, contacting various design consultants to develop solutions. Invariably, the resulting solutions were not optimized and required additional design modification. We quickly insisted that all RFIs go to all team members so that we could generate the best solution. While it initially seemed to take more time up front, it actually ended up saving us a lot of time and money by eliminating the need for multiple designs."

RICHARD V. PIACENTINI
Phipps Conservatory and Botanical Gardens

"Phipps was always very proactive with dialogue. They knew what questions needed to be answered early on. They didn't come to the Living Building Challenge asking what they could achieve or get for themselves, but focused more on how they could truly understand the nuance of the intent and reflect that in their project. As a team, they were a tight group that clearly had a lot of expertise and respect for one another. They approached the Challenge with grace."

EDEN BRUKMAN
International Living Future Institute

A PLAN TAKES SHAPE

Bringing all disciplines together to collaborate on a design plan is crucial for a Living Building, given the systems' complexities and interdependence. At the same time, integration ends up simplifying the process by answering many potential questions in advance. By the time the architect completes a schematic design, it includes all pertinent engineering, structural and landscaping details. This was the case with the CSL.

Although the planning for the CSL took far longer than traditionally designed projects, all participants agreed on the value of the extended early stage. Design charrettes wound down as fundraising efforts continued. In September 2008, Phipps held a ceremonial CSL groundbreaking and welcomed Heinz Endowments Chair Teresa Heinz to lead the event.

By September 2009, Minnerly and his colleagues at The Design Alliance Architects finalized the architectural drawings. It was now time to name the builder most qualified to help make the plans take shape. Unfortunately, the poor economic climate of 2008-2009 slowed fundraising efforts, so it wasn't until August 2010 that the construction was released for bid. When it was, Turner Construction was selected as the general contractor. Although Massaro Corporation had provided construction management and estimating services throughout the integrated design process for the CSL, it was always understood that the project would go out to bid once the design was complete. By December 2010, Turner's green site trailer was in place and the team was ready to break ground. The CSL was finally beginning to sprout.

37

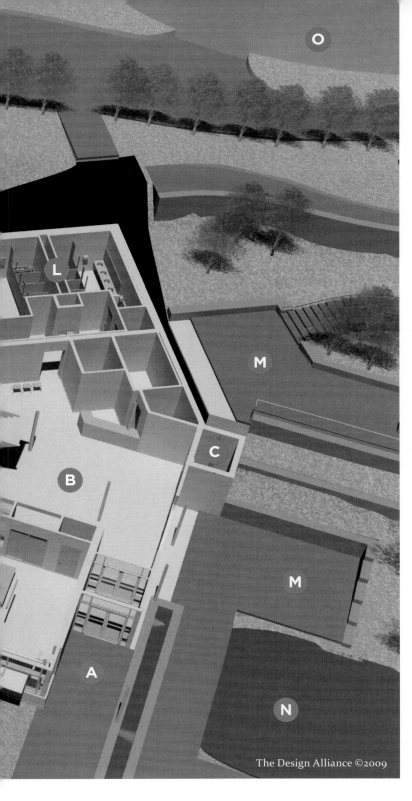

FIRST FLOOR PLAN

- **A** Entrance
- **B** Lobby Reception
- **C** Elevator
- **D** Classroom
- **E** Volunteer Area
- **F** Research/Open Office Space
- **G** Break Room
- **H** Conference Room
- **I** Exterior Stairs
- **J** Mechanical Room
- **K** Education Storage
- **L** Restrooms
- **M** Exterior Gathering Space
- **N** Lagoon
- **O** Tropical Forest Conservatory

"Traditional office buildings these days have big floor plates, but you can't get light into the middle of them. So we made the CSL long and thin in an effort to make that work. We looked at what the orientation of the building needed to be to get the daylight north, south, east and west. Considering all of that was one of the keys early on. It was a lot about energy."

L. CHRISTIAN MINNERLY
The Design Alliance Architects

39

Part II: **STRONG SEEDS**

The Design Alliance ©2009

SECOND FLOOR PLAN

A Lobby/Exhibit Space

B Green Wall

C Elevator

D Reception

E Conference Room

F Open Office Space

G Exterior Stair

H Break-Out Space

I Work Room

J Secure Files

K Restrooms

L Exterior Gathering Space

M Lagoon

N Tropical Forest Conservatory

"For us, it was a very important opportunity to rise to the Challenge and to be able to make this project happen. It was feasible because we had this very talented group of people committed to doing this in an integrated way and willing to check egos at the door. There's no ego in ecological design."

JOSÉ ALMIÑANA
Andropogon Associates

41

42

The Design Alliance ©2009

THIRD FLOOR PLAN

A Lobby

B Elevator

C Atrium Space

D Green Roof

E Exterior Terrace

F Rooftop Mechanical Unit

G Exterior Stair

H Lagoon

I Tropical Forest Conservatory

"I really liked the challenges posed by the Living Building Challenge. It clearly stated what we had to do so we went out and did it. There was beauty and simplicity to that. It helped inspire us to connect our food, health, sustainability and landscaping at Phipps. Because that's what the Challenge is all about — recognizing that everything operates within a system; everything is connected."

RICHARD V. PIACENTINI
Phipps Conservatory and Botanical Gardens

Part II: **STRONG SEEDS**

PART III

Shoots and Buds

Reaching for the Petals of the
Living Building Challenge

44

45

The following chapters of this book focus on the six individual Petals of the Living Building Challenge™ version 1.3:

1. **SITE**

2. **ENERGY**

3. **MATERIALS**

4. **WATER**

5. **INDOOR QUALITY**

6. **BEAUTY AND INSPIRATION**

The chapters are offered here according to the sequence in which they appear in the text of the Challenge, although the process of designing and constructing the Center for Sustainable Landscapes (CSL) did not follow a linear Petal-by-Petal path. There are aspects of each Petal in virtually every element of the building, as all members of the team wove multiple Petal Imperatives into their contributions to the project.

These chapters explore some of the CSL's Petal-specific challenges, obstacles, solutions and discoveries. Members of the design-build team weigh in on some of the many ways the project tested their professional assumptions — and sometimes their personal patience. In the words of Jason F. McLennan, "the Living Building Challenge is called a challenge for a reason."

For full text of the Living Building Challenge (including its six Petals and 16 associated Imperatives), please visit www.living-future.org.

NOTE: *In order for a project to receive full Living Building Challenge certification, it must provide performance data from at least 12 months of full operation after occupancy. This book was published during the CSL's first year, before the project was certified as a Living Building.*

47

THE SITE PETAL

Nurturing a Sense of Place

49

SUMMARY OF THE LIVING BUILDING CHALLENGE VERSION 1.3 SITE PETAL

Petal Intent

The intent of this Petal is to clearly articulate where it is acceptable to build and how to protect and restore a place once it has been developed and degraded.

Petal Imperatives

- Responsible Site Selection
- Limits to Growth
- Habitat Exchange

The Production Greenhouses and Tropical Forest Conservatory create a dramatic backdrop for the Phipps upper campus while workers clear the lower site for the future CSL.

SITE SPECIFICS

The Living Building Challenge Site Petal requires that physical structures be built in appropriate locations and in ways that protect and enhance the surrounding environment. In the case of the Center for Sustainable Landscapes (CSL), the geographic location was predetermined.

This third phase of Phipps Conservatory and Botanical Gardens' expansion was always intended to be constructed on one of the last remaining parcels of the public garden's larger campus: in the southwest corner of the property, nestled against a 30-foot slope behind the Tropical Forest Conservatory and Production Greenhouses, and adjacent to an obsolete Pittsburgh Department of Public Works storage facility and service yard. The CSL looks out over Junction Hollow to the west and Panther Hollow Lake to the south.

Situated in this area, the building fits beautifully into the overall footprint and vision of Phipps. It makes efficient use of land that was previously owned but not used by the organization, reclaims and restores an unused brownfield, and offers heart-of-the-city convenience for Pittsburgh's citizens and tourists.

51

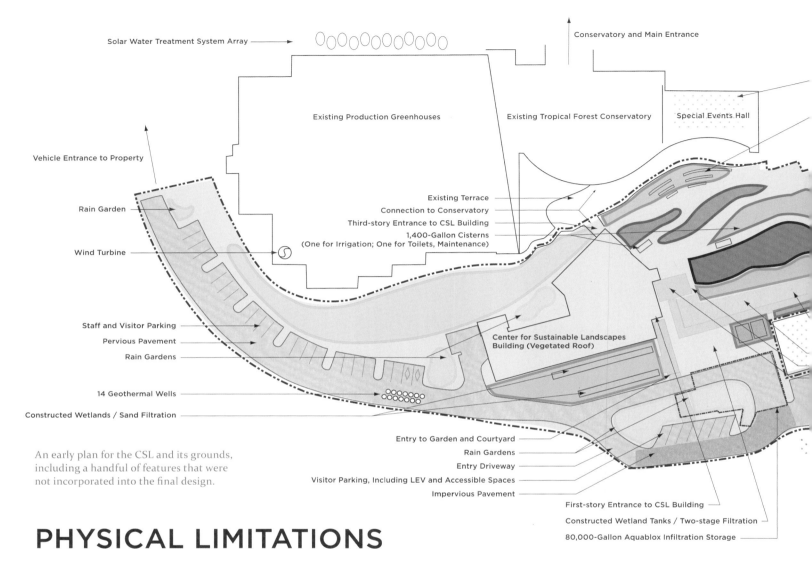

Solar Water Treatment System Array →

Conservatory and Main Entrance

Existing Production Greenhouses

Existing Tropical Forest Conservatory

Special Events Hall

Vehicle Entrance to Property

Existing Terrace
Connection to Conservatory
Third-story Entrance to CSL Building
1,400-Gallon Cisterns
(One for Irrigation; One for Toilets, Maintenance)

Rain Garden

Wind Turbine

Staff and Visitor Parking
Pervious Pavement
Rain Gardens

Center for Sustainable Landscapes
Building (Vegetated Roof)

14 Geothermal Wells

Constructed Wetlands / Sand Filtration

An early plan for the CSL and its grounds,
including a handful of features that were
not incorporated into the final design.

Entry to Garden and Courtyard
Rain Gardens
Entry Driveway
Visitor Parking, Including LEV and Accessible Spaces
Impervious Pavement

First-story Entrance to CSL Building
Constructed Wetland Tanks / Two-stage Filtration
80,000-Gallon Aquablox Infiltration Storage

PHYSICAL LIMITATIONS

There was no question about where the CSL would sit. However, there were numerous questions about how to make it work in its fixed location. The site's extremely tight geographic boundaries created stringent limits on where and in what orientation the structure could be situated.

All the team's specialists — architects, mechanical engineers, civil engineers, geothermal engineers, landscape architects and others — offered their ideas on how to meet the project's goals within the site's rigid physical parameters. They explored many different configurations of size, shape and orientation before landing on the building's final design: a 24,350 square foot, three-story, southwest-facing structure sitting on a 2.6-acre lot.

In addition, the team had to account for the elements of the project that would fall outside of the building's rectangular footprint but still within the boundaries of the site (such as surrounding landscaping, adjacent water collection tanks, geothermal well field, access driveways, etc.). As these various project goals intersected, so too did the Imperatives of multiple Living Building Challenge Petals. The team quickly learned that the Site Petal was not a stand-alone set of goals. Site-related design and planning decisions would inform strategies for the remaining five Petals, and vice versa.

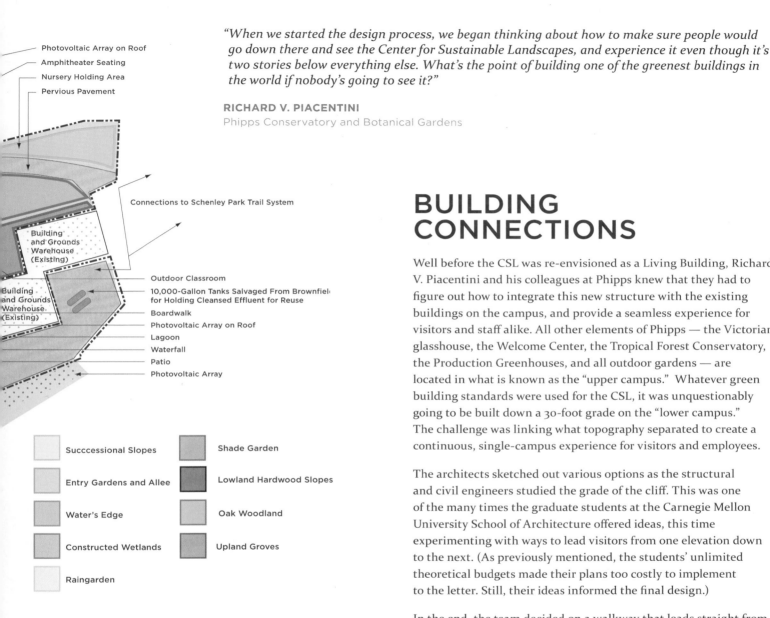

Photovoltaic Array on Roof
Amphitheater Seating
Nursery Holding Area
Pervious Pavement

Connections to Schenley Park Trail System

Building and Grounds Warehouse (Existing)

Building and Grounds Warehouse (Existing)

Outdoor Classroom
10,000-Gallon Tanks Salvaged From Brownfield for Holding Cleansed Effluent for Reuse
Boardwalk
Photovoltaic Array on Roof
Lagoon
Waterfall
Patio
Photovoltaic Array

Succcessional Slopes

Entry Gardens and Allee

Water's Edge

Constructed Wetlands

Raingarden

Shade Garden

Lowland Hardwood Slopes

Oak Woodland

Upland Groves

"When we started the design process, we began thinking about how to make sure people would go down there and see the Center for Sustainable Landscapes, and experience it even though it's two stories below everything else. What's the point of building one of the greenest buildings in the world if nobody's going to see it?"

RICHARD V. PIACENTINI
Phipps Conservatory and Botanical Gardens

BUILDING CONNECTIONS

Well before the CSL was re-envisioned as a Living Building, Richard V. Piacentini and his colleagues at Phipps knew that they had to figure out how to integrate this new structure with the existing buildings on the campus, and provide a seamless experience for visitors and staff alike. All other elements of Phipps — the Victorian glasshouse, the Welcome Center, the Tropical Forest Conservatory, the Production Greenhouses, and all outdoor gardens — are located in what is known as the "upper campus." Whatever green building standards were used for the CSL, it was unquestionably going to be built down a 30-foot grade on the "lower campus." The challenge was linking what topography separated to create a continuous, single-campus experience for visitors and employees.

The architects sketched out various options as the structural and civil engineers studied the grade of the cliff. This was one of the many times the graduate students at the Carnegie Mellon University School of Architecture offered ideas, this time experimenting with ways to lead visitors from one elevation down to the next. (As previously mentioned, the students' unlimited theoretical budgets made their plans too costly to implement to the letter. Still, their ideas informed the final design.)

In the end, the team decided on a walkway that leads straight from the terrace outside of the Tropical Forest Conservatory on the upper campus onto the green roof gardens of the CSL. From there, visitors may work their way down the terraced landscape via a gently sloping pathway or through the amphitheater and down stairs, eventually passing through all three levels to the greenery and lagoon below. This elegant solution continues the garden experience one has in the Conservatory and bridges the two halves of the campus.

"The site was tiny relative to what we were trying to accomplish and its funny geometry made it hard to work with. So we got everybody at the table and got all these people involved in trying to help understand how the building was going to integrate into this particular property."

L. CHRISTIAN MINNERLY
The Design Alliance Architects

53

The Site Petal: NURTURING A SENSE OF PLACE

"Because the brownfield site was previously developed, we ran into some challenges underground that you wouldn't find on a new construction site. We routinely found existing vaults and utility lines that weren't shown on historical drawings. This prompted the project team to use existing information and coordinated testing to figure out the best way to proceed."

JASON WIRICK
Phipps Conservatory and
Botanical Gardens

BEFORE

Building and planting on a brownfield meant that there was very little that could be retrofitted. The Andropogon Associates team had to find the best landscaping solutions given the existing circumstances.

AFTER

RESTORING A BROWNFIELD

To the southeast of where the CSL foundation would be placed sat an abandoned Department of Public Works (DPW) facility that had served the City of Pittsburgh in a variety of ways over the course of many years — perhaps as far back as the early 1900s. It had once housed stables for the city's equestrian squads; it was where the underground gas tanks were placed to store supplies for municipal fire and police vehicles; it had held inventory for the Oakland District's salt trucks; and it had been paved over numerous times. As such, the DPW building and its surrounding land had suffered from decades of environmentally devastating development.

Still, the team knew it needed to take advantage of this precious extra real estate in some way — for storage and/or maintenance use — though they were not sure how best to proceed. First, team members considered demolishing the existing DPW structure and removing the debris to rebuild something new on the site, perhaps tying it architecturally into the CSL. At another point, they even thought about renovating it as a Living Building and constructing a new maintenance facility nearby.

Eventually, they determined that the best solution was to salvage what they could of the DPW structure, refurbish it to meet higher performance standards, and allow it to support the living systems of its next-door-neighbor, the CSL. It now serves as the official maintenance facility for the entire Phipps campus and its rooftop is the home of one of the CSL's three photovoltaic solar arrays.

However, the process of getting this space up to current standards was not without its challenges. Cleaning out the underground tanks was key to giving new life to the DPW site and to freeing up containers now used to collect spillover water for the CSL's sanitary system. But getting the site ready for construction proved to be more difficult than expected, as the entire brownfield was littered with previously unreported systems. In addition, the entire 2.6-acre lot was paved over with asphalt. When construction workers encountered obstacles that hindered their ability to continue the task at hand, they stopped what they were doing, consulted other members of the team, and determined the best way to move forward.

At the same time, the team focused on how to convert an unsightly brownfield into the surroundings of the greenest building on the Phipps campus. The land itself would host important systems — maintenance storage, water tanks and geothermal wells, to name a few. But it also needed to further the aesthetic impact of the CSL. Members of the Andropogon Associates landscaping team had their work cut out for them when it came to beautifying what was once poisoned and abandoned. And, while landscaping the brownfield was only a small portion of the overall site development strategies applied to the CSL, it represented a critical goal of the Living Building Challenge: to restore previously used sites instead of developing pristine land.

"The old DPW service yard had a completely opposite feel to it. Here was this previously developed brownfield and we were trying to turn it into something beautiful that felt like it had always been there. It was different than working with a site that already has a lot of natural features. We were absolutely starting from nowhere."

L. CHRISTIAN MINNERLY
The Design Alliance Architects

A LANDSCAPE TAKES ROOT

Andropogon Associates' José Almiñana led the CSL landscaping effort. He and his colleagues set out to enhance the project with organic surroundings that echoed the dual missions of the Living Building Challenge and Phipps, seeking local plant and soil materials that were indigenous, beautiful and inspirational.

Andropogon worked closely with Phipps staff and other consultants to scavenge whatever they could from the brownfield and incorporate those materials into their overall plan to plant the hillside and grounds wrapping around the CSL. Among the site's features:

- A terraced garden leads down the hill from the roof to the ground floor of the CSL, allowing visitors to enter the building on three different levels and experience an ongoing connection between the interior and the exterior.

- More drought-resistant plants are placed on the higher levels of the site, where water is less available, while plants with more water needs are positioned on lower elevations, where gravity enables a more constant source of natural irrigation.

- Three distinct soil profiles support the landscape, with deeper soils designed to encourage water to infiltrate the ground water table, a middle layer that retains moisture to contribute to the health of plant structures, and a top layer with organic matter that enables plant growth.

- A programmable fountain at the ground-floor level visually draws visitors through the site and allows them to play as they learn about the site's net-zero water systems.

- A permaculture garden on the green roof of the CSL highlights plants that are edible, medicinal, functionally useful (such as switch grass for biofuel) or educational (to be incorporated into children's programming).

- Five dedicated rain gardens keep stormwater out of the municipal sewer lines, allow it to be infiltrated, and educate visitors about the simplicity of such systems.

- A green wall and aquarium are planned for the interior of the atrium to demonstrate how aquaponics works. In a recirculating system, waste water from the fish will provide fertilizer for the plants, which will then clean the water before it returns to the fish. As an added benefit, the plants will also help purify the air in the atrium.

57

PLAYING WITH TIME

The CSL's landscape, like the building it surrounds and the natural cycle it celebrates, evolves over time. Almiñana designed the landscape so that it will not only change, but actually improve with maturity, presenting increased opportunities for visitors to relate to it more closely as time progresses. Whether taking in the natural aspects of the CSL's exterior or viewing the landscape through a window from the interior, guests and occupants are meant to experience a biophilic connection with these living, growing forms. Time, in this context, is akin to a building material. Once time itself is incorporated into the site, the project will be fine-tuned to adapt to its conditions. In this way, people, landscapes and operational systems will all re-calibrate as needed to accommodate the changes introduced by the changing seasons and the passing years.

"Buildings can incorporate living things, living shapes, things that remind us of life in their structures. But at the end of the day, what we connect with is life forms — things that are truly derived from life. And the more we connect with a landscape, the better the landscape gets."

JOSÉ ALMIÑANA
Andropogon Associates

THE PARKING ISSUE

As much as the CSL team liked the idea of making Phipps a car-free destination, they knew it was unrealistic to bar vehicles completely from the campus. Many members of the visiting public arrive by car, as do some staff and other individuals coming to Phipps for business purposes. There was no doubt that parking spaces were needed to accommodate those cars, but the question was how to provide them without giving automobiles undue emphasis within the CSL landscape.

They realized that the best solution would be found once they shifted their expectations and recognized that they could not do everything they wanted to do — or not do — with regard to parking. They decided to create limited parking on the lower campus adjacent to the CSL and reserve those spaces for people who have business meetings with staff working in the building. All Phipps visitors, including those who are only coming to the CSL on the lower campus, may park in any of the various parking lots on the upper campus and enter through the Conservatory. Phipps created two electric vehicle charging stations and priority parking for carpools and energy efficient cars, and also encouraged every employee to take public transportation or ride bicycles to work. Those employees who do drive park in a dedicated lot beside the campus.

59

PLANTING NARRATIVE

"For every one of the landscape options we considered, we had a potential different site-specific circumstance that we had to respond to. We looked at how to right-size and right-place everything, and asked how to find the most elegant solutions, while offering myriad opportunities for people to come and learn about landscapes."

JOSÉ ALMIÑANA
Andropogon Associates

A Constructed Wetlands

B Rain Garden

C Entry Gardens

D Lowland Hardwood Slope

E Upland Groves

F Water's Edge

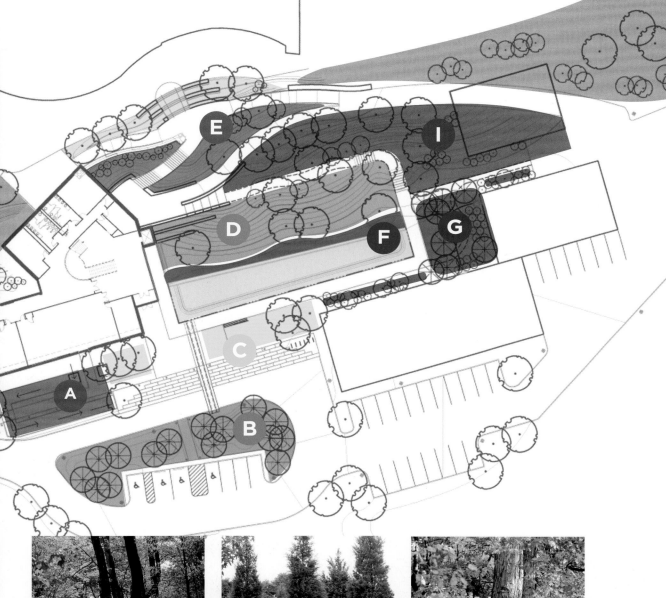

G Shade Garden **H** Successional Slopes **I** Oak Woodland

61

The Site Petal: **NURTURING A SENSE OF PLACE**

HABITAT EXCHANGE

This Living Building Challenge Imperative dictates that each acre of development should be offset by an acre of land that can be set aside for at least 100 years as part of a habitat exchange. However, the International Living Future Institute sometimes waives this requirement if the project site is a remediated brownfield. Since Phipps undertook such a project with existing onsite underground fuel storage tanks, cleaning and re-purposing them for water storage and treatment, the CSL project was eligible for an exemption.

"Out of the Challenge's 16 Imperatives from version 1.3, 13 of them had a relationship to sites and landscapes, which we were very pleased to see. It reassures us that it's a rating system that actually does good by placing significant weight on sites and landscape systems and recognizing that all these things go together."

JOSÉ ALMIÑANA
Andropogon Associates

Phipps has three green roofs, including one that houses this vegetable garden.

62

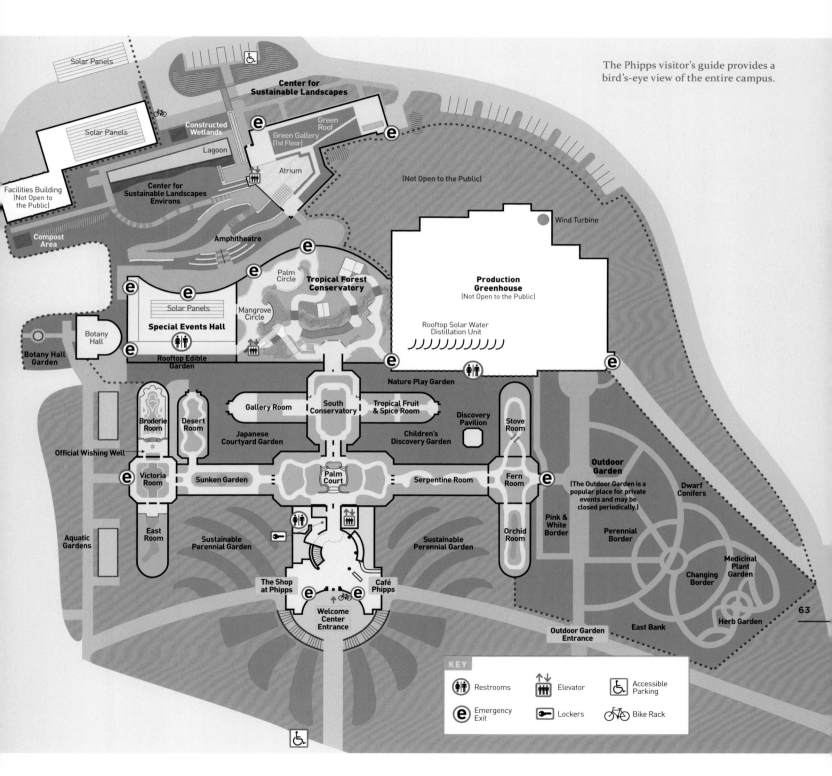

The Phipps visitor's guide provides a bird's-eye view of the entire campus.

Solar Panels

Solar Panels

Center for Sustainable Landscapes

Constructed Wetlands

Green Roof

Green Gallery (1st Floor)

Lagoon

Atrium

Facilities Building (Not Open to the Public)

Center for Sustainable Landscapes Environs

Compost Area

Amphitheatre

(Not Open to the Public)

Wind Turbine

Palm Circle

Tropical Forest Conservatory

Production Greenhouse (Not Open to the Public)

Solar Panels

Special Events Hall

Mangrove Circle

Rooftop Solar Water Distillation Unit

Botany Hall

Botany Hall Garden

Rooftop Edible Garden

Nature Play Garden

Gallery Room

South Conservatory

Tropical Fruit & Spice Room

Discovery Pavilion

Stove Room

Broderie Room

Desert Room

Japanese Courtyard Garden

Children's Discovery Garden

Outdoor Garden (The Outdoor Garden is a popular place for private events and may be closed periodically.)

Dwarf Conifers

Official Wishing Well

Victoria Room

Sunken Garden

Palm Court

Serpentine Room

Fern Room

Pink & White Border

Perennial Border

East Room

Aquatic Gardens

Sustainable Perennial Garden

Sustainable Perennial Garden

Orchid Room

Medicinal Plant Garden

Changing Border

The Shop at Phipps

Café Phipps

Welcome Center Entrance

Outdoor Garden Entrance

East Bank

Herb Garden

63

KEY

👫 Restrooms	🛗 Elevator	♿ Accessible Parking
ⓔ Emergency Exit	🔑 Lockers	🚲 Bike Rack

The Site Petal: **NURTURING A SENSE OF PLACE**

THE ENERGY PETAL

Powering the Organism

The Energy Petal: **POWERING THE ORGANISM**

SUMMARY OF THE LIVING BUILDING CHALLENGE VERSION 1.3 ENERGY PETAL

Petal Intent

The intent of this Petal, with its single Imperative, is to signal a new age of design, whereby all buildings rely solely on renewable forms of energy, and operate year in and year out in a pollution-free manner. Since renewable energy sources are currently more expensive than energy efficiency measures, extreme efficiency as a first step is assumed.

Petal Imperative

Net-Zero Energy

"When I think about what's been the easiest Petal, energy is what comes to mind for me. Once the building was designed, the net-zero energy imperative was relatively straightforward from our side of things."

WILLIAM BECK
Turner Construction

"There's an interesting dynamic with a net-zero project. For every kilowatt hour you add to the building's energy consumption, you add first costs. So it completely changes the discussion when it comes to the cost-effectiveness of the energy efficiency strategies that you're trying to implement."

MARCUS SHEFFER
7Group

THE IMPORTANT FIRST STEP

With only a single Imperative, this Petal has a precise goal: achieve net-zero energy on the site of the Center for Sustainable Landscapes (CSL). If money and land were limitless, any project could get there — in theory — by installing enough photovoltaic solar arrays to meet demand. But the CSL team had to be more strategic.

So they started with efficiency, exploring every opportunity to minimize the building's energy loads. Everything was included in the research: the envelope, orientation, glazing, roof, insulation, lighting, heating, cooling, plug loads, laptop vs. desktop computers and employee comfort levels at different indoor temperatures. Using this information, the team calculated how much energy was really needed and how much free energy was available at the site before exploring various technologies that would help the building meet its own power requirements.

Not surprisingly, the architects and engineers had to collaborate very closely on the energy strategy. Alan Traugott and his colleagues at CJL Engineering led the mechanical engineering efforts for the project. Their driving philosophy was to tighten up the building as

much as possible and drive down the energy from the outside in as a way of minimizing the size of the systems needed to power it.

Working through several integrated design charrettes, and involving multiple consultants, the team established a project performance target for energy consumption of no more than 20,000 British thermal units (Btu) per square foot per year (20kBtu/sf/yr). Next, they ran energy models to evaluate whether or not the building could operate within that energy footprint. With all efficiency strategies utilized, the team found that the numbers consistently came up at approximately 19.2kBtu/sf/yr. Establishing 20kBtu/sf/yr as a target would rank the CSL among the most energy-efficient buildings in the country. All of the experts agreed that it was an appropriate goal for such a revolutionary project.

67

> *"The engineers did a lot of work interviewing staff to find out exactly how they work. We asked how many staff will be in the building, where will they be, what hours of the day will they be there, will they be there on the weekends, will they bring in lunch or go out to eat, will they be recharging devices. We even talked about encouraging people to dress for the seasons so we can minimize the amount of heating and cooling energy we needed."*

RICHARD V. PIACENTINI
Phipps Conservatory and Botanical Gardens

> *"Passive first, outside in, good envelope, good glass, overhangs, and lots of daylight. If you don't have that kind of orientation for the building and get all team members playing on the same card, you're not going to end up with a building that's optimized specifically for net-zero energy."*

ALAN TRAUGOTT
CJL Engineering

ORIENTATION AND PASSIVE ENERGY

The way that the CSL would sit on the building site would profoundly affect its energy characteristics, so it was important for the design to take full advantage of all available free energy — including daylighting, passive solar heating and natural ventilation. With this in mind, the project team set out to create the optimal design, which included adequate shading, good insulation values and glass that let in daylight without transferring heat or excessive solar load.

In order to achieve their goals, the team began to sketch the CSL on a long east-west axis using the north and south sides as the major façades containing the bulk of the building's glazing. This orientation would allow for good sun control, while overhangs and shading on the south wall would prevent unwanted heat gain and glare — especially useful in the summer months when the sun sits high in the sky. On the north side, the team allowed for as much diffused light as possible to enter the building by adding a generous amount of windows. On the east and west façades, the sun would shine directly into the building in the early and late hours of the day, potentially creating heavy cooling loads — particularly in the afternoon — as occupants adjusted interior controls to manage glare, heat and humidity. To guard against that potential energy draw, the team incorporated minimal glazing on the east and west sides to help control the sun's light, while the adjacent landscaping was carefully chosen and positioned to further reduce cooling loads. (Deciduous trees placed in these locations provide shade in the summertime, while their bare branches allow sunlight into the building during the winter.)

A vertical axis wind turbine capable of generating 10,000 kilowatt hours of energy each year supports the CSL's net-zero energy mission.

Natural light bathes the CSL interior.

"*Daylighting influences the energy to a significant degree. When you start doing modeling on any project that seeks to be energy efficient, you use the model to guide your design decisions relative to load reduction. We spent a lot of time analyzing these load reduction strategies early in the modeling process, which ultimately led to the level of insulation, the kinds of windows that are used, the amount of glass that's in the building, etcetera.*"

MARCUS SHEFFER
7Group

70

Light finds its way in from all angles, starting at the top of the building's atrium.

LETTING THE LIGHT SHINE

L. Christian ("Chris") Minnerly knew that the CSL daylighting strategy would be one of the most important factors to influence the design and affect energy usage. He and the engineers decided to focus first on how the building could make the most of natural daylight as a way of minimizing the need for artificial light.

In typical office buildings, up to 40 percent of total energy consumption goes toward interior lighting. With this statistic in mind, the team conducted careful analysis of how to maximize daylighting performance in the CSL. They worked toward a goal of 80 percent daylight autonomy and at least 30 foot-candles from daylight in the majority of the occupied space so that ambient lighting needs would be met without using electricity during most business hours. This strategy would also help meet the part of the Living Building Challenge stipulating that

any occupied interior space must be in close proximity to both daylight and operable windows.

The research yielded data that the team could use to reduce other internal energy loads as well. These energy models then helped shape decisions related to the building envelope, insulation, window types and ventilation, as they all contributed to the building's total energy profile.

71

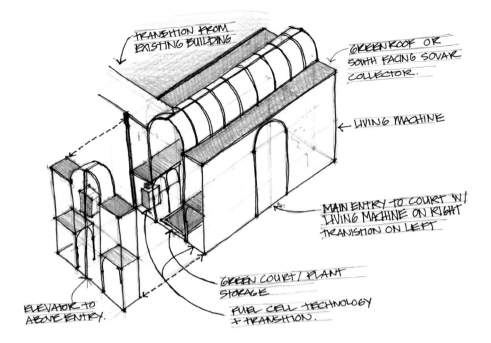

A professional rendering of Piacentini's napkin sketch, which includes ideas (such as the living machine concept) not incorporated into the final CSL design.

TRANSITION FROM EXISTING BUILDING

GREENROOF OR SOUTH FACING SOLAR COLLECTOR.

LIVING MACHINE

MAIN ENTRY TO COURT W/ LIVING MACHINE ON RIGHT TRANSITION ON LEFT

GREEN COURT / PLANT STORAGE

FUEL CELL TECHNOLOGY + TRANSITION.

ELEVATOR TO ABOVE ENTRY.

A BURNING POSSIBILITY

Early on in the design process, the project engineers considered many different renewable energy sources that could power the CSL. One idea was to use a micro-turbine for electricity and heat generation, effectively placing a mini power plant on site that would be fueled by biomass readily available on the Phipps campus. The thought was that leftover plant material from Conservatory flower shows, exhibits and garden maintenance could be combined with food waste from Café Phipps and catered events, and then put into an anaerobic waste digester for conversion into methane. This methane, in turn, would be used to run the micro-turbine.

But there was only one problem: The Living Building Challenge™ strictly prohibits combustion in any form on the site of a registered project. Still, the CSL team was convinced that a micro-turbine would help meet the project's overarching goals, so it decided to try to persuade the International Living Future Institute (ILFI) to make an exception. For the appeal, Traugott represented the design team, contending that the system would use renewable resources and build efficiencies into the project that justified the combustion needed to run it. He also argued that it would require far less real estate than photovoltaic solar arrays and raised a significant question: Since the Challenge allows for projects to pull power from the municipal grid provided that their annual net use is zero or less

and the grid's power comes from burning coal and natural gas, isn't it a contradiction not to allow any form of on site combustion?

In the end, despite the team's case for exemption, the ILFI stood firm and refused the request for a variance since it would set a problematic precedent — mostly because combustion in any form produces particulates and carbon emissions. Furthermore, promoting non-combusting renewable energy supports this nascent industry while driving down cost and acceptability with no harmful emissions at the site. So, after receiving this final ruling, the team returned to the charrettes to find new solutions that would work. They ultimately determined that three forms of renewable energy would power the CSL: geothermal, solar and wind.

"In the summer, when we need to reject heat, we reject it into the earth. In winter, we extract that heat and warm up the building. In the in-between seasons, we're simultaneously pulling and dumping heat into the geothermal loop within the building. On a micro-macro scale, we're transferring energy from one room to the other."

CRAIG DUDA
CJL Engineering

GEOTHERMAL

Geothermal represents a significant chapter in the project's energy story. During the design phase, the team knew it wanted to utilize geothermal technology — using the earth's constant 55-57 degree Fahrenheit temperature to provide free heating and cooling service to the building — but there were different ways to achieve that end. Originally, team members explored the possibility of a distributed system, in which multiple half- to four-ton heat pump units would be scattered throughout the building. But they later determined that a consolidated system with one centrally located heat pump would better serve the building's needs.

As the team proceeded, the challenges of the project quickly became apparent. Given the CSL's tight site parameters, the driveway area offered the only real estate sufficient to locate the geothermal wells' six-inch boreholes, which must be set 20 feet apart to be effective. But even there, the space was limited. So the choice was made to go deeper than the typical 300-350 feet as a way of getting more capacity out of each well while reducing the total number of wells. The team eventually opted to install 14 wells, each 510 feet deep and filled with a water-glycol solution to provide freeze protection. A loop of polyethylene (PEX) tubing runs down the length of each borehole to provide the heat exchange circuit for the well, tying back into the building systems. Each well acts as a 20-foot diameter thermal storage column of soil that slowly absorbs rejected air conditioning heat over the summer and then recovers that heat for the building to use in the winter.

The geo-exchange process requires a good seasonal balance between the hot and cold months to result in an approximately equal amount of heat that is added and withdrawn over the course of the year. The CSL's geothermal system was designed to use 60-70 percent less energy than a traditional heating-ventilation-air-conditioning (HVAC) system because it stores heat and cooling rather than having to generate it.

The CSL's geothermal system takes advantage of the stable underground 55-57 degree Fahrenheit temperature, where the ground is no longer interacting with the atmosphere.

73

The Energy Petal: **POWERING THE ORGANISM**

"One of the challenges with a net-zero building is load matching. By sending power up the hill, we don't have to worry about that. It allows us to use every kilowatt the PV system produces; then we take the energy we need when we need it. The upper campus is basically a big battery."

ALAN TRAUGOTT
CJL Engineering

SOLAR

There are three photovoltaic solar arrays (PVs) on the CSL site: one on the roof of the Special Events Hall, one on the roof of the maintenance building adjacent to the CSL, and a third ground-mounted unit on the edge of the cliff overlooking Panther Hollow. (Situating the ground-mounted array amid an existing stand of trees and working around underground utilities required some fine-tuning to determine the ideal location and orientation to avoid shading.) No panels were installed on the top of the CSL itself since that space was reserved for a green roof; however, all arrays, except for the ones atop the Special Events Hall, are visible from the building interior.

Together, the three arrays (all American-made) are expected to produce 135,000 kilowatt hours of power for the CSL annually. But seasonal variations mean that solar energy is more plentiful in the summer than in winter. In the sunniest

months, the system generates more energy than what the building can use at any one point. So the engineering team needed to come up with a workable load-matching alternative. Rather than return surplus power to the municipal utility ("net metering"), they chose to put it to use on site.

With Phipps' sizable main campus located just up the hill, the CSL is in an ideal position to send its solar energy to the larger facility, which can always absorb the maximum amount the PVs are capable of delivering. The power travels through the Conservatory transformer, where it serves both upper and lower halves of the property. The CSL then draws the power it needs from the larger supply, which is projected to be less than what its PV arrays generate on an annual basis. At the end of each year, Phipps is expected to use every kilowatt produced by the photovoltaics.

Collectively, the three sets of PV arrays on the Phipps campus are capable of generating 135,000 kWh of power annually.

WIND

Phipps takes its position as a sustainable design leader seriously, so the organization welcomed the idea of installing a wind turbine on the site as an adjunct energy generator. Engineering calculations revealed that the photovoltaic solar arrays would produce more power than what was needed to run the CSL, but the wind turbine technology would round out the energy story for the campus, serving important educational and demonstration purposes.

An American-made 10 kW aluminum vertical axis wind turbine now sits above Panther Hollow, where it can take advantage of the most favorable wind conditions. On an annual basis, it has the potential to generate approximately 10,000 kilowatt hours of electricity, which is fed to the upper campus transformer. The model produces more electricity than traditional propeller-style turbines with the same swept area, it creates energy with winds as low as four miles per hour, and its slim profile makes it safer for birds and bats.

"The most challenging part of the project was finding enough room for the ground-mounted solar array and the wind turbine. But we worked through it and in the end, everything fit together like puzzle pieces."

JOE MORINVILLE
Energy Independent Solutions

Phipps' powerfully elegant wind turbine.

<blockquote>
"Just as medicine has seen major technological improvements over the past 20 years, so has HVAC. To advance medicine, doctors must implement new ideas. To advance HVAC, engineers and building owners must also implement unconventional technologies and combinations. The success of projects like the CSL makes the uncommon common, so that we experience an improvement in our overall quality of life, just as with medicine."
</blockquote>

GEORGIA BERNER
Berner International Corp.

The CSL's highly efficient HVAC unit, which sits atop the building's green roof, was manufactured just 50 miles from Pittsburgh in Newcastle, Pennsylvania.

A DOWNSIZED MECHANICAL SYSTEM

The intense collaboration between architects and engineers resulted in the CSL's ultra-efficient and right-sized energy system, produced by Berner International Corp. Given the quality of the envelope, glazing, light shelves and shading — combined with the strong contributions of the chosen passive sources — the CSL was well-primed to get away with smaller HVAC system components. Reducing the size of the pump, compressor and fan meant, of course, that wires, ducts and pipes could also come down in size, bringing the overall energy draw down with it. As yet another example of the interrelationship among the Living Building Challenge's various Petals, this more modest HVAC system also helps meet the project's energy goals while reducing its materials volume.

<blockquote>
"As we went through, we looked at various options for heating and cooling equipment, but once you're limited to all-electric, the options become somewhat limited. One of the most efficient electric systems is a ground-source heat pump system, which is what we ended up with."
</blockquote>

MARCUS SHEFFER
CJL Engineering

FRESH AIR

As plans for the CSL unfolded, it became very apparent that the project needed to incorporate a heating and cooling system that allowed for a healthy amount of natural ventilation. To achieve this goal, the engineering team conducted in-depth computational fluid dynamics studies to optimize the location, number and size of the building's windows, and to situate them within the building envelope to maximize air flow within the interior. Testing various temperature profiles both inside and outside of the building, the engineers found that a combination of upper and lower window openings would provide the best circulation into the space. Additionally, the narrow shape of the structure would enable good air manipulation, particularly when both tiers of windows are open on the north and south sides.

For more on the phase change material and how it factored into the project's Red List discussion, see page 97.

"It's interesting to me that a century ago, people designed buildings with high and low windows that allowed for the best natural ventilation in interior spaces. But since air conditioning came along, we seem to have forgotten how to do that. Now, we're re-discovering what people knew and designed a long time ago."

RICHARD V. PIACENTINI
Phipps Conservatory and Botanical Gardens

Phase change material installed in selected walls and ceilings of the CSL helps regulate interior temperatures naturally by absorbing and releasing heat as it transitions back and forth between solid and liquid states.

PHASE CHANGE

Relatively late in the construction process, Richard V. Piacentini was concerned about a change that had been made in the plan for the CSL's atrium. Originally, the atrium was designed with a significant amount of concrete, which would act as thermal massing. However, that plan was adjusted to keep the construction schedule on track and the concrete was set to be replaced by drywall and studs.

In a conversation with Carnegie Mellon University's Vivian Loftness, Piacentini learned about a new soy-based phase change material that had recently been introduced to the market. Loftness explained to him that the new material is capable of adding thermal mass to portions of a building using very little thickness and weight. With a melt point of 73 degrees Fahrenheit, it uses a change in state to release and absorb a vast amount of heat relative to the mass it contains. In the winter, it releases heat into the space at night. In the summer, with the addition of nighttime flushing, it helps keep the interior cool. In short,

Piacentini felt it could replace the concrete that had been engineered out of the CSL while further reducing the building's energy demand.

When Piacentini went to the project team and proposed that the phase change material be used in the CSL, members agreed that it would be a good fit. It was ultimately added behind the atrium walls and above the drop ceiling in the office areas.

For more on the phase change material and how it factored into the project's Red List discussion, see the Materials section on page 92.

The interior of the CSL atrium.

"Our original plan was to passively heat and cool the atrium since the primary purpose of most atriums is to serve as a transition space from the outside to the inside of the building. Why waste energy heating and cooling such a space? But over the course of construction, we decided that we would need to use the atrium as our primary visitor interpretation space. Once we did that, we realized we would have to condition the space. We felt that our passive cooling strategy would still work. However, keeping the space warm in the winter would be an issue and we needed to come up with a way to efficiently heat the space."

RICHARD V. PIACENTINI
Phipps Conservatory and
Botanical Gardens

79

> *"Normally, you put in some thermostats, humidistats and CO2 sensors for demand control ventilation. But it's central and limited to different spaces, maybe a couple of offices or conference rooms. Khee Poh's study is beyond that — it gets down to the individual person and how they're acting and what their comfort ranges are. It's getting down to the nitty gritty of how the building is performing."*

ALAN TRAUGOTT
CJL Engineering

The University of Pittsburgh's Dr. Melissa Bilec engages in an idea exchange about sustainable building solutions with a group of One Young World delegates in the CSL classroom.

A STUDY IN HUMAN AND BUILDING BEHAVIOR

As progress was being made on the CSL, Phipps made the building available as a test bed in affiliation with a research grant given to the University of Pittsburgh Mascaro Center for Sustainable Innovation and the Carnegie Mellon University Center for Building Performance and Diagnostics by the National Science Foundation Emerging Frontiers in Research and Innovation. Led by the University of Pittsburgh's Dr. Melissa Bilec and Carnegie Mellon University's Dr. Khee Poh Lam, the research enabled by this grant allows the professors and their graduate students to study the intricacies of the CSL's performance and make detailed predictions about the ways in which the building reacts to interior occupants, as well as to exterior conditions.

Dr. Bilec and her students focused on environmental life cycle analysis, while Dr. Lam and his students set out to study the building's performance. Collectively, the group began its work with the understanding that buildings are subject to real-time changes in external micro-climatic conditions and internal occupancy use patterns so the state-of-the-art computational models they developed go further than standard measurement verification. In fact, they actually aim to continuously predict building performance and optimize energy consumption while ensuring occupancy comfort within various dynamic operational scenarios throughout the life cycle of the building. This information will also be used to understand the long-term environmental impacts due to construction and use.

The research ultimately prompted the installation of sensors and metering devices inside of the CSL. The equipment monitors the indoor environmental and systems performance, and delivers adjustments according to individual occupancy patterns, measuring temperature, humidity and air quality fluctuations given different activities, routines and schedules. Now that the building has opened, the data are used to validate the computational models and clarify how the building actually behaves. By tuning the system to anticipate the CSL occupants' needs based on the predictive analysis done specifically by Lam and his students, the building will now be able to continuously minimize energy use while maintaining the desired comfort zones.

> "People build green buildings all of the time but, in most cases, nobody knows if they really work. We have offered our building to local universities to use as a lab so that they can test it, see how well it is working, and use what they find to develop or try out building technologies of the future."

RICHARD V. PIACENTINI
Phipps Conservatory and Botanical Gardens

> "The CSL is really the perfect green building scenario. You have the literal green (the landscape) blending, mapping and integrating with the built environment. So the natural and the built environments are being displayed in an interactive way at all levels. This is such an exciting opportunity to really demonstrate the full extent of what is possible for all future buildings that aim to be sustainable."

KHEE POH LAM
Carnegie Mellon University School of Architecture

81

"People can see that if they use the elevator to go up instead of taking the steps, there's an energy penalty for that and here it is. We've provided lots of meters and made the building very sophisticated. Users will know where their energy is going."

CRAIG DUDA
CJL Engineering

"The dashboards will allow Phipps to see on an annual basis how much energy they're using, and see it go up and down on a daily basis. They'll understand those daily and seasonal fluctuations."

ALAN TRAUGOTT
CJL Engineering

CONSTANT FEEDBACK

Dashboards throughout the property report on the CSL's real-time energy use, allowing occupants and visitors to track the building's daily, monthly and annual energy patterns — including what it generates and what it uses. The trends also reveal how the CSL is performing on an annual basis, tracking where it is relative to its net-zero goal. Instantaneous metrics quantify what the photovoltaic solar arrays, geothermal system and wind turbine produce, as well as what the building and its occupants consume. Operations personnel who monitor the reports on lighting, computer loads, HVAC pumps, site lighting and other areas use these data to make subtle adjustments to the property's energy profile as needed to maintain the proper balance.

PLUG LOADS

Calculating the CSL's anticipated plug loads required making certain assumptions about annual usage. Desk lights, copiers, computers and cell phone chargers would all get plugged in, turned on and switched off multiple times throughout a normal day. Pre-occupancy modeling would provide an anticipated range of use, but actual demand would need to be monitored closely once the building became operational. Now that the building is occupied, if usage figures spike unexpectedly or begin to gradually rise, the CSL's monitoring systems report the change so that the source of the energy draw can be traced.

"You make assumptions on the overall annual average use for different components. But they're only assumptions, so it's something you have to monitor. The CSL's occupants will see on a regular basis if there's an unusual occurrence. If there's a blip in the plug loads for equipment or computers, it will prompt somebody to check to see what's different. The whole idea of breaking down the energy usage into those very detailed components is so they can understand the impact of that behavior, and then compensate and adapt."

ALAN TRAUGOTT
CJL Engineering

Interactive dashboards offer background information and real-time reports on the CSL's performance systems.

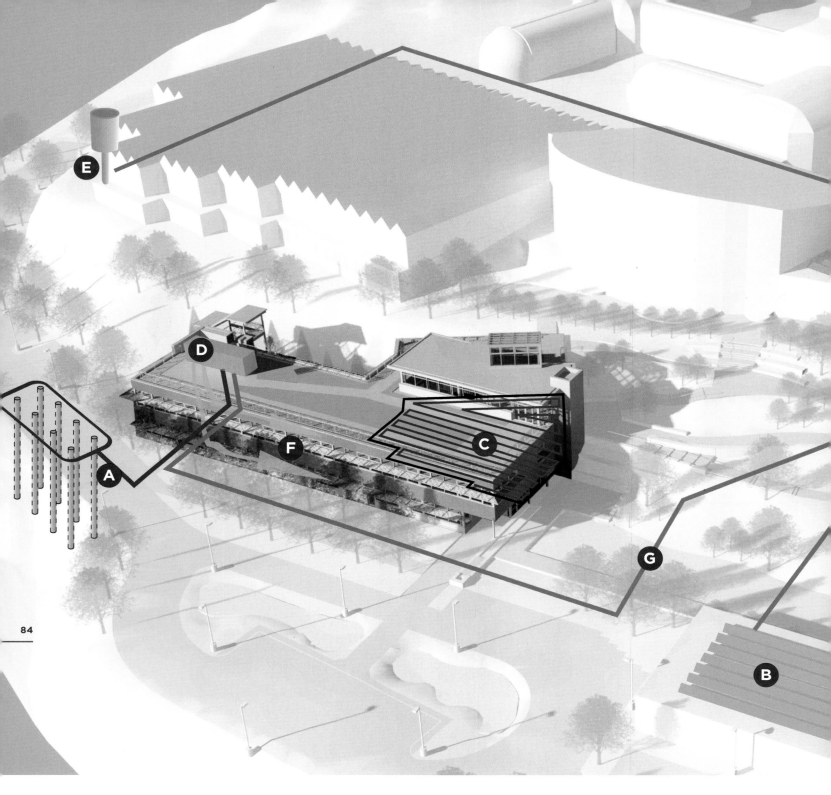

84

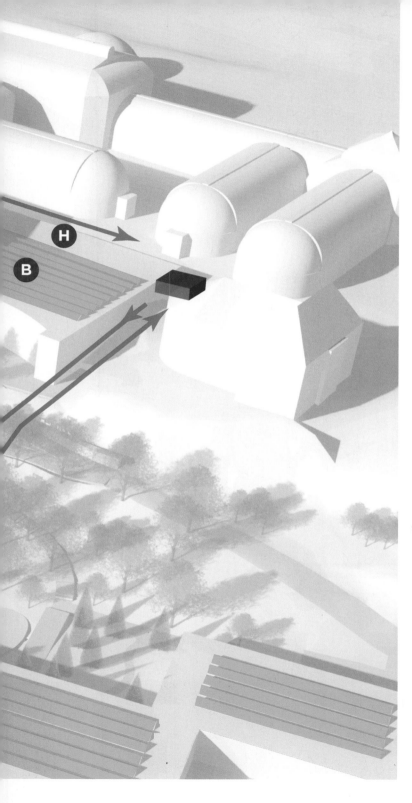

"We tried to model as carefully as possible to understand where and how we would use energy in order to determine what that net-zero equation would be. We looked at how much we'd use per year, how much we'd make up with renewables and how big the PV system would have to be in order to accomplish the net-zero process. It was a collaboration with everybody deciding what those approaches would be."

ALAN TRAUGOTT
CJL Engineering

NET-ZERO ENERGY

A Geothermal Wells

B Photovoltaic Array

C Hot Water Radiant Floor

D Rooftop Mechanical Unit

E Wind Turbine

F Under Floor Air Distribution

G 100 Percent CSL Electric Supply

H Excess Power to Campus

DAYLIGHTING
SOUTH WING

- **A** Sun Shade
- **B** Light Shelf
- **C** Operable Blinds
- **D** Sloped Ceiling
- **E** Green Roof

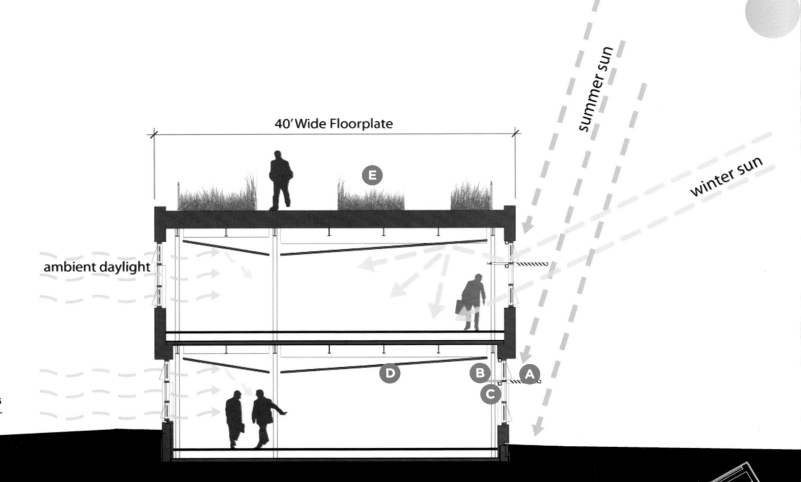

summer sun

winter sun

40' Wide Floorplate

ambient daylight

NATURAL VENTILATION

ATRIUM

SOUTH
WING

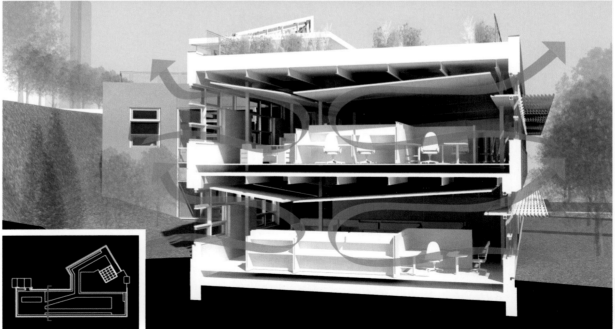

The Energy Petal: **POWERING THE ORGANISM**

THE MATERIAL PETAL

Constructing a New Paradigm

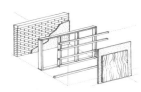

5

SUMMARY OF THE LIVING BUILDING CHALLENGE VERSION 1.3 MATERIALS PETAL

Petal Intent

The intent of this Petal is to remove, from a health and pollution standpoint, the worst known offending materials, and to reduce and offset the environmental impacts associated with the construction process.

Petal Imperatives

- Materials Red List
- Construction Carbon Footprint
- Responsible Industry
- Appropriate Materials/Services Radius
- Leadership in Construction Waste

> *"The Materials Petal was probably the most eye-opening of everything that's in the Challenge. Conserving energy and water makes sense to people, but I don't think people really realize all the toxic chemicals that we use every day. It's shocking and scary when you look at what we put into the buildings where we live and work."*
>
> **RICHARD V. PIACENTINI**
> Phipps Conservatory and Botanical Gardens

COMPELLING THE INDUSTRY TO CHANGE ITS WAYS

The Living Building Challenge Materials Petal is arguably the most revolutionary, as it calls upon the marketplace to make the most profound changes. Other elements of the Challenge require technology and funding, along with a healthy dose of innovation. But the barriers to the Materials Petal are industry wide.

With very few exceptions, the design-build world is ill-equipped to answer the call for a truly environmentally friendly material and supply chain. Worse, due to the global sourcing of most building materials' various components, manufacturers are largely unable to answer the question, "What are the ingredients in your products?"

The Living Building Challenge shines an uncomfortably bright light on this basic issue. It urges the professions to look more closely at the materials they use — then do what is necessary to obtain full disclosures from manufacturers — in order to create sustainable structures. Working together, architects, engineers and builders have the power to establish a more rational, responsible materials economy. As one of the earliest Challenge projects, the Center for Sustainable Landscapes (CSL) had a more difficult road to travel in order to meet this requirement.

91

"We kept thinking, 'How is it going to be possible to have this quality control when the project was bid in a conventional way?' Unlike LEED, if you make a mistake and you get wood that's not certified, it just means that you lose that point. But with the Living Building Challenge, the thing that was hanging over us was that you can't have any mistakes. If you miss a single Imperative, you won't get the certification for that Petal at all."

MARC MONDOR
evolveEA

THE RED LIST

At the heart of the Petal lies the Red List, a tally of 13 "forbidden" materials and chemicals that are prohibited — with only a few exceptions — in or on a Living Building Challenge project. For the CSL team, materials proved to be the Challenge's most difficult Petal and the Red List proved to be the Materials Petal's most difficult Imperative. The International Living Future Institute (ILFI) has since found this to be a common refrain among virtually all teams that have accepted the Challenge.

It was easy enough to specify zero-VOC paints, for example. But when it came to specifying for the entire building — every wall, floor, door and window — the team discovered exactly how complicated the Red List would make their jobs. L. Christian ("Chris") Minnerly and his colleagues at The Design Alliance Architects conducted in-depth research and created a preliminary materials matrix with supplies they considered to be Red List-friendly. However, as the project progressed and construction began, questions about materials slowed or halted the momentum. Even when appropriate materials were identified, contractors sometimes came on site and attempted to substitute materials with which they were familiar (or that were more affordable).

When Turner Construction was selected as the CSL's general contractor, consultants from evolveEA stepped in to introduce them to the nuances of the Living Building Challenge. The consultants provided a high-level overview of the program and how it differed from Leadership in Energy and Environmental Design® (LEED) and other standards. Then they drilled down to the Challenge's specific Imperatives, placing particular emphasis on the Red List since Turner would bear most of the responsibility for documenting and installing approved materials. When Turner later brought subcontractors onto the site, they performed the same type of training.

At this time, evolveEA also created a series of cover sheets summarizing each of the project's three certification programs — the Living Building Challenge, LEED® and Sustainable Sites Initiative™ (SITES™) — to help Turner Construction and its subs identify compliant materials. These summaries helped the construction team track and document the proper ingredients for the building. Since Turner had bid the job on a lump-sum basis, this was a critically important tool.

92

"The Red List is one of the reasons everybody talks about how it's neither easy nor cheap to make a Living Building."

L. CHRISTIAN MINNERLY
The Design Alliance Architects

Sandstone used on the hillside behind the CSL was locally sourced by Raducz Stone Corporation in Butler, Pennsylvania.

"In my estimation, only about 15 or 20 percent of the suppliers had the information to know which materials would really comply. Turner had incredible difficulty getting the materials information that they needed. When they couldn't get it from suppliers, they had to call on manufacturers directly."

JOSEPH NAGY
evolveEA

93

A 60-DAY SPECIFICATION PERIOD

94 **L. CHRISTIAN MINNERLY**
The Design Alliance Architects

Minnerly and The Design Alliance Architects team specified a large number of the building materials during the design development phase. But when Turner Construction came onto the project, there were still a fair amount of products to identify and it was clear that this would continue to be a time-consuming exercise. The worry was that construction would begin before all goods were vetted and materials concerns would hold up progress.

As a result, they decided to add an unprecedented step to an already unprecedented project. Turner was given a 60-day spec period so that they could conduct the entire submittal process prior to, rather than during, construction. During that time, Turner went through

every remaining product slated for the job and sought the proper documentation to validate its compliance with the Challenge.

It was a monumental undertaking and one that many team members might allow more time for if they had it to do over again. Turner Construction worked diligently to research and document the CSL's complete materials list, but many manufacturers were either unwilling, or unable, to disclose complete ingredient lists for their products — particularly within the 60-day timeframe. In those cases, Turner went deeper into the manufacturing chain in search of answers. When there were none, they changed course and pursued replacement products.

95

> *"Manufacturers are not usually prepared to provide the information required to demonstrate compliance with the Red List and distance sourcing requirements. Standard product literature, websites and MSDS sheets just don't contain that kind of information. Red List assurances require higher level authorization and legal review to deal with company disclosure concerns. So that really extended our efforts when it came to material vetting and selection, as well as the submittal preparation and review process."*

JOSEPH NAGY
evolveEA

INTERACTING WITH MANUFACTURERS

The difficulty with seeking answers about the toxicity of materials and whether or not those materials complied with the Living Building Challenge was that, in most cases, the questions had never been asked before. It made sense to the CSL team that manufacturers were largely unaware of the Challenge, as it was still such a new initiative. But team members were surprised to hear so many manufacturers tell them that they would not, or could not, identify the full list of ingredients in their products.

In some cases, product components came from elsewhere and manufacturers did not have access to the level of detail required for Challenge documentation. In other cases, suppliers were reluctant to disclose complete information. Sometimes, alternate products had to be found. But occasionally, the team's efforts led to tangible change when manufacturers heard that their products could not be used on the site unless they were reconfigured.

> *"The more we talked to them and explained the Living Building Challenge, the more willing they were to talk to us about changing their products. Setting these new standards is forcing a lot of manufacturers to change what they're doing. They want to make their products sustainable."*

MEGAN CORRIE
Turner Construction

> *"Fabric protectors, flame retardants, formaldehyde. This stuff is in everything and it's not the kind of thing you want bio-accumulating in your body. We just didn't want any of it in the building. You don't start thinking about these things until you get involved in a project like this."*

RICHARD V. PIACENTINI
Phipps Conservatory and
Botanical Gardens

SHORT STORIES WITH BIG IMPACTS

There are numerous examples of the CSL team shifting directions along the way in order to meet the Challenge's Materials Imperatives. These are just a few of them:

LIGHT SHADES The sun supplies the majority of the building's interior light, so it was important to be strategic when it came to shading. Too much shading would reduce the ambient light levels provided by daylighting; too little would mean glare in the summer months and excess heat gain. So Minnerly designed a mix of automatic and manually operated shades capable of providing shading when needed. But after much research, there were no products on the market that met both the architectural specifications and the Red List Imperative. All had low levels of halogenated flame retardant, which carries with it significant human health impacts. Eventually, the CSL team requested and received an exemption from the ILFI to use a product with a small amount of flame retardant (since there appeared to be no viable alternative), but Piacentini declined the offer, saying he didn't want it in the building. The team then heard about a new solar powered system being developed in Europe that could reflect light into an interior space. At the time of this book's publication, that system was being considered for the CSL's windows.

DOORS The CSL team discovered just how many modern doors are manufactured with Red List chemicals. The team members went in search of wooden doors to meet the original design specification, but found nothing but products containing formaldehyde in the glues holding together the doors' internal components. They considered going with glass doors instead, which would be aesthetically pleasing but much more expensive. Hollow metal doors would have met the Challenge requirements; however, they would not provide an elegant solution consistent with the look and feel of the project. (There are some doors of this type in the building that help satisfy local fire codes.) Then the team heard about a Pittsburgh office building where the wooden doors were going to be thrown away as part of a renovation. The project team ended up salvaging those doors, reconfiguring the hardware, recalculating the swings, and patching them as needed. With one changed design decision (following an arduous set of steps), they rescued materials bound for a landfill, repurposed local materials and satisfied a Challenge requirement.

96

PHASE CHANGE MATERIAL For the walls and the ceiling of the CSL's atrium, the team needed a way to regulate the amount of heating and cooling that passed through the space and worked in tandem with the concrete thermal mass. During construction, Richard V. Piacentini heard about a new soy-based phase change material that he felt certain would provide a workable and sustainable solution. The project team contacted the manufacturer to check on the product's compliance with the Red List. Although the company's representatives were certain their product was made without toxic chemicals, they agreed to conduct a thorough audit of all ingredients. In so doing, they learned that a minimal amount of halogenated flame retardant was sandwiched between the product's outer layers. However, the CSL team still felt strongly that the product would suit the project, so it requested an exemption. Since the toxic content was deep within the phase change material's interior, the ILFI consented. But the ultimate positive effect of this situation was that the manufacturer has since pledged to remove the dangerous chemical from this otherwise green product. This example demonstrates both an underlying intent of the Living Building Challenge — to remove harmful chemicals from otherwise good products as a way of eliminating toxins from the built environment — and the game-changing power of a single project team.

FURNITURE The Challenge does not currently cover the contents of a building, so furniture is exempt from its requirements. Still, Piacentini and his Phipps Conservatory and Botanical Gardens colleagues wanted the CSL's interior to be as green as its exterior. They went in search of desks and chairs that would comply with the Red List. It turned out to be a challenging proposition. Modular furniture's laminated surfaces contain formaldehyde, and cushioned chairs have fabric protectors containing polytetrafluoroethylene (PTFE) and halogenated flame retardants. Everywhere they looked, they came across furniture that fell below the high standard they wanted to maintain. But they persevered, eventually finding a system of workstations using Forest Stewardship Council (FSC)-certified wood veneer surfaces and overhead cabinet fronts, along with work surface substrate upgraded to meet no added urea formaldehyde (NAUF) standards. They also opted for recyclable chairs that meet Level 2 or 3 standards as established by the Business and International Furniture Manufacturer's Association with no fabric protectors or flame retardants.

97

"The more people do what we did when we insisted on non-toxic products, the faster we're going to get changes in the industry. Nobody's going to change unless people demand it."

RICHARD V. PIACENTINI
Phipps Conservatory and Botanical Gardens

SHARING THE DISCOVERIES

As more project teams seek non-toxic building materials — whether they are pursuing Living Building Challenge certification or just committed to environmentally friendly practices — the databases of suitable products will continue to grow. When construction began on the CSL, however, there were no official resources available and the team had to do its own due diligence as it went. (Pharos and Green Wizards were both up and running, but neither offered the depth of information needed to specify the entire job.)

Because the CSL was one of the first projects to accept the Challenge, there were very few people in the professions who could offer first-

hand advice regarding some of the questions that arose. Still, any exchange of ideas would be helpful. The CSL team turned to the Living Building Community Dialogue, an online forum created by the International Living Future Institute (ILFI) for individuals involved in registered Challenge projects. The Dialogue allows professionals to communicate, ask questions and share their discoveries. It also offers the opportunity to interact with ILFI staff. While the Dialogue was new and its content was more limited when the CSL was under construction, it has continued to expand as more projects have accepted the Challenge.

CONSTRUCTION CARBON FOOTPRINT

To achieve the Materials Petal's second Imperative, Phipps collaborated with faculty and students at the University of Pittsburgh to conduct a comprehensive life cycle assessment (LCA) of the CSL's assembly and operations, and calculate its approximate carbon footprint. This research will continue for the first several years of the building's occupancy and is designed to measure the CSL's footprint while also informing the LCA measurement process. The ILFI recognizes the imprecise nature of LCA work (given the often outdated and/or incomplete data available for use with assessment), so it carefully reviews all Living Building Challenge project offsets.

RESPONSIBLE INDUSTRY

The Living Building Challenge requires that all wood used for projects be certified by the FSC, come from salvaged sources, or be intentionally harvested on site. The industry is adapting to the growing demand for FSC-certified wood, so the CSL team had less difficulty with this Imperative. Still, the Challenge's wood requirements are different than those of LEED, so additional documentation was required for the CSL.

For the timber boardwalk that surrounds the lagoon, it took some effort to locate wood that was FSC-certified and locally sourced, all while meeting the design specifications. In the end, Turner Construction reached out to various mills before finding an appropriate and acceptable solution.

While preparing to install grade stakes, the construction team faced another difficulty when it discovered that they were not made from FSC-certified wood (although the socks were). Locating a replacement product would have caused unnecessary delays, so, instead, the team chose to salvage allowable wood from a nearby project and cut its own stakes on site. The original grade stakes that came with the socks were then recycled.

99

"The expertise you need for our climate is best understood by people who have worked and practiced in our climate. It's time for us as a sustainable design community to invest in regionalism and in regional expertise. It's time to honor the experts in our own backyard."

VIVIAN LOFTNESS
Carnegie Mellon University School of Architecture

"The idea behind appropriate sourcing is to try to use appropriate building materials for the region like it was done thousands of years ago. It can be difficult to find local materials that work well in construction. In the northeast, we can expect masonry and materials like that but it requires a different type of thinking to find local materials that are conducive to the architecture and the aesthetic of a project."

MARC MONDOR
evolveEA

APPROPRIATE RADIUS

The underlying intent of the Challenge's radius Imperative is to encourage healthy regional economies, while reducing the environmental impact of shipping goods over great distances. The heavier the physical object, the closer to the project it should originate. The more local the contributions, the better (although ideas can come from anywhere). In a place like Pittsburgh, where there is a deep pool of local talent and a rich history of manufacturing, one might think it would be easy to keep products and services local. But this was yet another example of the CSL project's complexity.

It was a top priority for Piacentini and the Phipps organization to make the CSL a celebration of Pittsburgh talent. The core design, engineering and consulting team came from within the city limits or from elsewhere in Pennsylvania, so it was not difficult to achieve the goal of keeping consultants within a 1500-mile radius. But building the CSL using only materials and technologies that stayed within the Living Building Challenge-specified zones was trickier — as was documenting the provenance of everything that was used. (By the time the team needed to research and report on material origins, version 2.0 of the Challenge had been published. The updated version was less ambiguous when it came to the definition of appropriate sourcing, so the

team requested and received permission to follow the requirements of that Imperative instead.)

The project's heaviest components — the panels for its photovoltaic solar arrays — were manufactured 2,585 miles away in Hillsboro, Oregon, while the inverters were made in Denver, Colorado, traveling 1,450 miles to Pittsburgh. But despite these distances, they still ultimately fell within the Challenge's radius allowance since renewable energy technologies may travel as far as 9,000 miles. The arrays' heavy steel and aluminum racking, however, came from nearby Ambridge, Pennsylvania (a distance of 20 miles) and Youngstown, Ohio (70 miles away).

HILLSBORO, OR

DENVER, CO

PITTSBURGH, PA   500 MILES   1,000 MILES   1,500 MILES

101

The Materials Petal: **CONSTRUCTING A NEW PARADIGM**

"LEED and the Living Building Challenge work well together. LEED looks at best practices that are easily implementable and as those practices become standard, it slowly raises the bar. The Living Building Challenge sets the bar very high and asks people to attempt to attain it. That educates the marketplace about where things are going. There's a really productive relationship between LEED and the Living Building Challenge in moving the marketplace jointly. The Red List is a clear example of this, as it has allowed LEED to begin to include adverse health impact materials in some of their credits."

JOSEPH NAGY
evolveEA

102

CONSTRUCTION WASTE

**For the CSL, Turner Construction took the lead on meeting
the Living Building Challenge's requirements on responsible
construction waste management. This Imperative can only
be achieved when the construction team is clearly committed
to the goal of generating less waste from the beginning.**

When it comes to construction waste, the Challenge starts where other green building standards leave off because it specifies exactly what percentage of each type of waste must be diverted from landfills. Since the CSL aimed to satisfy the requirements of the Challenge along with SITES certification (which calls for slightly different soil handling measures than the Challenge) and LEED, the project's construction waste had to be handled and documented very carefully.

In order to meet this goal, EvolveEA worked with Phipps and Turner to identify which of the local co-mingled construction waste handlers was best equipped to support the project's goals. After screening all vendors, they chose the one with the most experience on green job sites and the most sophisticated understanding of the inherent complexities involved in documenting the process. Before any waste was recycled or discarded, however, the team engaged a local nonprofit organization specializing in construction material reuse to visit the site and identify what they could salvage and resell to other builders, organizations or homeowners. The final hurdle was handling foam insulation and carpet scraps, which had to go through a separate vendor qualified to recycle those specific types of substances.

103

THE WATER PETAL

Nourishing from Within

The Water Petal: **NOURISHING FROM WITHIN**

SUMMARY OF THE LIVING BUILDING CHALLENGE VERSION 1.3 WATER PETAL

Petal Intent
The intent of this Petal is to realign how people use water in the built environment, so that water is respected as a precious resource.

Petal Imperatives
• Net-Zero Water
• Sustainable Water Discharge

TRICKLES OF CHANGE

The Water Petal is one of the Living Building Challenge's most profound, as it reaches beyond the boundaries of a single project to effect change on a much broader scale. Net-zero water on an individual site is just the beginning; the Petal is intended to realign the way water is used throughout the built environment.

Luckily for the Center for Sustainable Landscapes (CSL) team, Pittsburgh is a water-rich region of the country. At the same time, the idea of reducing water demands on the campus of a conservatory housing thousands of plants with enormous irrigation demands seemed a bit ironic. But the Challenge asked for the CSL to deliver net-zero water performance within its own perimeter at a minimum, regardless of the needs of Phipps Conservatory and Botanical Gardens' upper campus. Still, the project's philosophy was to look at whole systems and do whatever possible to connect seemingly distinct operations — whether between performance areas of the Challenge or between the two halves of the Phipps campus.

Meeting the Challenge for the CSL, therefore, meant designing an overall water-balanced approach, incorporating all three tiers of water that would need to enter and exit the building: potable water (suitable for drinking and hand-washing), greywater (drain runoff) and blackwater (contaminated by human waste). Rather than look at any of these sources as an individual net-zero problem, the team explored comprehensive solutions that would yield net-zero total usage for the entire site and fit the appropriate quality of water with its intended use.

107

The Water Petal: **NOURISHING FROM WITHIN**

BRAINSTORMING

During initial planning charrettes, the CSL team considered various options as they aspired to net-zero water. Team members discussed installing a 200,000-gallon water cistern on the lower site to use as a thermal mass for heating and cooling, but this proved to be cost-prohibitive. They considered running organic waste from toilets and kitchens through a digester to produce methane, but calculations revealed that the site would not yield enough waste to make the plan economically feasible. (Even if they gathered organic café waste from nearby universities to run through a more substantial digester, the site would not accommodate equipment large enough to meet the necessary capacity.) They pondered using a system similar to a Living Machine® as a way to treat wastewater — an idea incorporated into Piacentini's original napkin sketch of the CSL — but later decided that constructed wetlands would be a better fit for the site and help meet the project's goal of connecting the building to the landscape. They even thought about processing waste from the entire Phipps campus (beyond the boundaries of the CSL)

through constructed wetlands on the site, but the necessary square footage was simply not available.

As the team moved forward, questions continued about how to make the best use of the substantial amount of rainwater that flowed down to the CSL from Phipps' upper campus and then exited the property via the combined stormwater-sewer discharge lines. Suddenly, it became clear that the CSL project had an opportunity to significantly decrease the overall site's overflow while also satisfying the Challenge.

Establishing a baseline, the team began to identify a solution by looking at how much stormwater they could realistically capture on site via rain gardens, underground tanks and constructed wetland lagoons. Their calculations revealed that a combined system was capable of holding back an entire seven-year storm event if properly designed. Only at the 10-year point would water overflow out of the combined system. Next, they figured out how to use the captured water for the building's various water needs.

"When it comes to Phipps, there's a certain amount of credibility that comes along with it. The local plumbing and public health officials know what the true intent is. They know this project is about doing things the right way and establishing new and innovative processes. There might have been more skepticism if these requests had been coming from a developer simply looking to save a dollar by doing something different."

MICHAEL TAKACS
Civil & Environmental
Consultants, Inc.

Stackable crates wrapped in geotextile fabric were installed below the rain gardens and paving as a way to take on lagoon overflow.

108

A 1,700-gallon underground cistern stores rainwater captured from rooftops on the Phipps campus until it is needed for greywater and irrigation use.

DRAWING FROM THE CITY FOR POTABLE WATER

The Living Building Challenge allows municipal water to be delivered to a project for consumption purposes only if the local jurisdiction restricts onsite water treatment for potable use. The City of Pittsburgh, like many jurisdictions, requires a building to become its own water authority if it seeks to supply its own potable water. The CSL team opted to accept potable water into the site through municipal lines that feed the entire Phipps campus. When they looked at the project in its entirety, they felt that they would actually capture and clean far more water than they would ever extract from the municipal system, which would more than justify their draw from city sources and help meet the overall net-zero goal.

"Before this, Phipps only used municipal supplies for their water needs. Now we have a large reservoir of water that we can repurpose."

MICHAEL TAKACS
Civil & Environmental Consultants, Inc.

109

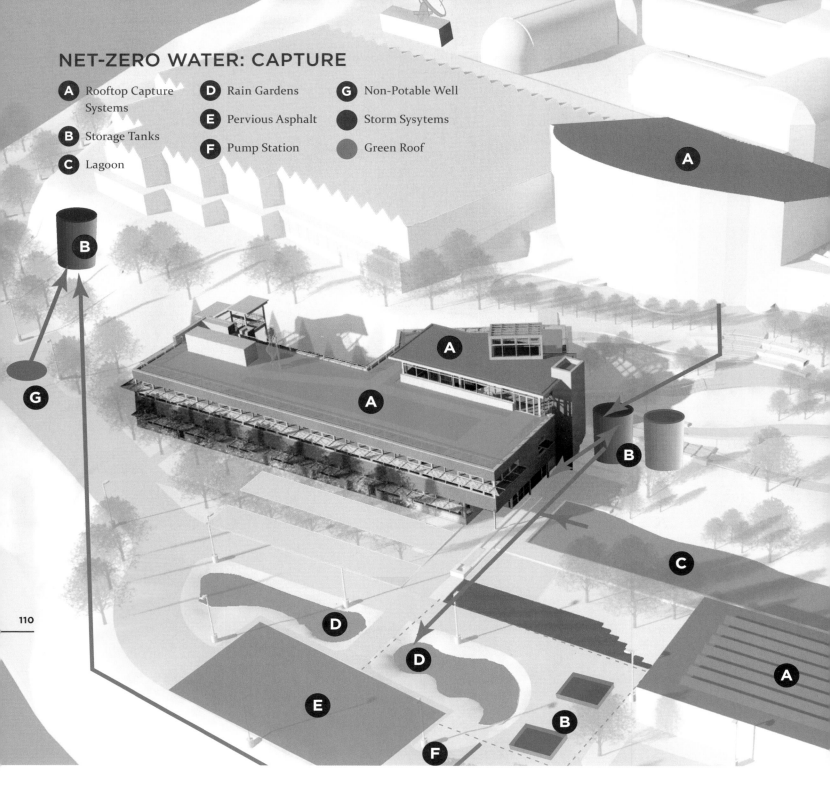

NET-ZERO WATER: CAPTURE

A Rooftop Capture Systems

B Storage Tanks

C Lagoon

D Rain Gardens

E Pervious Asphalt

F Pump Station

G Non-Potable Well

● Storm Sysytems

● Green Roof

110

COLLECTING WHAT FALLS FROM THE SKY

At the heart of the CSL's water strategy is its multi-layer storm- and rainwater capture strategy. The systems are separated based on how water is reused (for irrigation as opposed to sanitary purposes), but there is a certain level of redundancy among the systems that allows water to be pulled from one system to serve another, if needed. Rain that gets reused on the Phipps campus falls onto clean surfaces — glass rooftops, landscaped fields or healthy wetlands — before continuing its journey through the site's sophisticated water treatment system.

- The substantial rooftop space atop the Tropical Forest Conservatory is ideal for collecting the nearly 40 inches of average annual precipitation that hits Pittsburgh.

- Captured rainwater from the Conservatory roof flows into a 1,700-gallon underground cistern that supplies the initial water for flushing toilets and for irrigation.

- The CSL's own third-floor roof provides another surface space where rainwater may be collected.

- The maintenance building roof (host to the photovoltaic solar arrays) also sends rainwater into the system.

- A lagoon captures overflow from the cistern and surface runoff from most of the site and from the adjacent roofs.

- The lagoon overflows into underground rain tanks covered with permeable groundcovers and part of the site access road. These stackable milk crate-style units are wrapped in a geotextile fabric to provide structure strong enough to accommodate vehicle traffic, while being porous enough to provide significant carrying capacity.

- The underground rain tanks are divided into two sections for a combined 80,000 gallons of capacity. Tanks capable of storing 64,000 gallons of water are lined so that the cleaner runoff from the site can be captured and used for irrigation. Another 16,000 gallons of storage tanks are unlined and designed to capture runoff from the road. In the summertime, when this water is relatively clean, it can also be channeled into the lined rain tanks and used for irrigation. In the winter, when there is a chance of contamination by road salts, the water can infiltrate into the ground.

- Sanitary water is cleaned on site with a constructed wetland and sand filters. After the water is cleaned, it is pumped to another 1,700-gallon cistern, where it is used to flush the toilets.

111

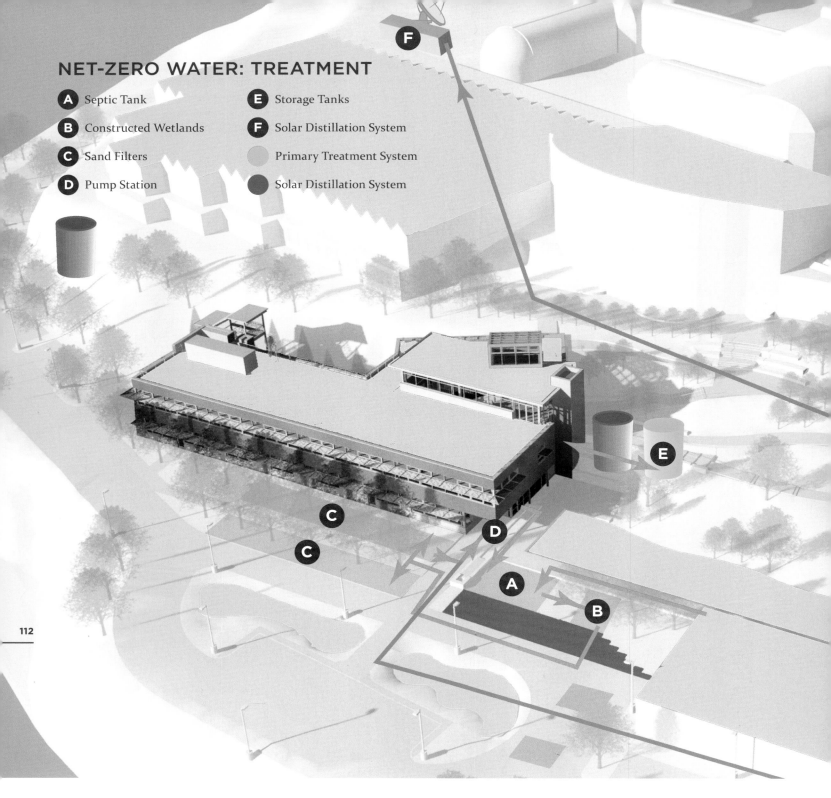

NET-ZERO WATER: TREATMENT

A Septic Tank

B Constructed Wetlands

C Sand Filters

D Pump Station

E Storage Tanks

F Solar Distillation System

Primary Treatment System

Solar Distillation System

"From an architect's perspective on the design, we realized early on that with this tight site and lots of grade changes, constructed wetlands would be an appropriate solution for the project. It also made sense because it embodied the spirit of Phipps. It demonstrates how the landscape integrates into the building; how the building and the landscape become one singular machine."

L. CHRISTIAN MINNERLY
The Design Alliance Architects

USING WETLANDS TO TREAT BLACKWATER

The water used to flush the toilets in the CSL cycles through a closed loop system that begins and ends on site, drawing nothing from the municipal supply. Water initially captured from the roof of Phipps' Tropical Forest Conservatory is used to flush the toilets in the CSL and flows into a tank on the exterior grounds. Solids settle out and liquid effluent travels to one of two constructed wetland treatment cells. The wetlands' plants help uptake most of the nutrients in the liquid effluent, which then passes through a series of treatment sand filters before working its way into a pump tank that returns the water to a reuse holding tank. Here, the water is continually cycled through an ultraviolet filter until pumps draw the filtered greywater back up into the building, where it is used once again to flush toilets and the cycle begins anew.

In order to enhance the function of the wetlands, plant species were carefully chosen for their ability to thrive in nitrogen-rich environments. Those selected for the CSL site include a variety of grasses, reeds, bulrushes and other plants typically found in natural wetlands.

113

IRRIGATION HELPS MEET NET-ZERO GOAL

Water needed to irrigate the CSL's green roof and its interior plants requires the least amount of treatment. The system pulls greywater from one of the underground storage tanks, runs it past a UV filter to be cleaned (but not purified to potable standards), and delivers it to hose bibs throughout the site.

But as the project team designed the water strategy for the CSL, engineers had to take into consideration the fact that the site would collect more water than it would need for its own irrigation uses. So as team members continued to calculate existing and projected water usage, they sought solutions that would balance what the CSL system would capture with what the building and landscape would use. And, because the Living Building Challenge restricts water from going back into the municipal storm system, they had to make sure that the excess water would infiltrate the ground rather than have it flow back into the sewer.

The original water strategy called for unlined underground storage tanks capable of collecting approximately 60,000 gallons of stormwater, which would then seep into the ground (rather than flow back through municipal pipes). Then two things happened. First, a new water engineer came to the project and determined that the original calculations were too low, and the project actually needed to add another 20,000 gallons of rainwater storage to meet the Challenge. Second, in the process of drilling the geothermal wells, the driller discovered that there was enough water underground to supply a well capable of producing 20,000 gallons of water per day.

Then Richard V. Piacentini got an idea: Since Phipps uses around 20,000 gallons of water daily to water plants in the Conservatory, why not take water harvested at the CSL and use it for irrigation on the upper campus rather than let it seep into the ground? Simply capturing rainwater in the underground tanks would only offset a couple of months' worth of irrigation, he thought, which would not be financially feasible. However, supplementing with a well would mean Phipps could offset all of the irrigation water with more than seven million gallons per year.

He approached the team with a request to add a 20,000-gallon cistern on the upper campus that could hold one day's worth of water and line the underground rain tanks rather than let their contents seep into the ground. They could supplement the cistern on the upper campus with the contents of a well on the lower campus when the rain tanks were empty. Initially, the team raised concerns about the idea because the Challenge does not typically allow projects to use well water. Also, they worried that if the rain tanks were full at the time of a storm, the excess water would overflow into the sewer lines and the CSL would lose the Challenge.

Piacentini requested that the team calculate the rate at which the water stored underground would infiltrate into the ground. Their answer: approximately 20,000 gallons daily. So why not draw off that amount every day and use it for irrigation purposes on the upper campus? This way, the organization could use the water just as quickly as it could infiltrate, drawing down Phipps' overall water demand from the City of Pittsburgh. Using captured stormwater, combined with well water, would create a supplemental irrigation supply capable of delivering more than seven million gallons to the Conservatory annually. Wouldn't it make sense to "scale jump" if it meant reducing Phipps' annual municipal draw of potable water by such a vast quantity when treated greywater was perfectly suitable? So the team requested — and received — a variance from the International Living Future Institute (ILFI) to allow for water stored within the boundaries of the CSL site to be pumped to, and used in, the Conservatory — a solution that fits into the Challenge's scale-jumping protocol.

Ultimately, the ILFI and the CSL team agreed that what is appropriate for Pittsburgh might not be the same as what works in Houston, Seattle or any other part of the country. Rainfall varies, as do water use needs. The key is to define what net-zero means for each distinct project, then work to implement solutions to achieve specific goals. In the case of Phipps, the CSL is capable of harvesting far more water than it needs for the lower campus and pumping irrigation water to the upper campus (which falls outside of the Challenge project scope) helping to offset the building's overall intake of municipal potable water. As calculated, the net use is zero or less.

Six rooftop distillation units capture and treat
water used for Phipps' orchid collection.

SURPLUS WATER FINDS A ROOFTOP HOME

Once engineers ran the numbers for the full spectrum of water reuse strategies, it was clear that they were repurposing nearly all of the water waste that was coming out of the CSL. But not every last drop. Every day, the system ended up with approximately 150 gallons of potential excess effluent water from the sanitary loop. The team considered disposing of it on site through a traditional infiltration process, but the soils were not conducive to such an approach and the Department of Environmental Protection denied the request. The team then explored the possibility of spray-applying it in the greenhouse, but that was not permitted either. Pushing it back into the municipal sewer would mean losing the Water Petal, so some solution had to be found. That is when Piacentini heard about an innovative water distillation product that could help the CSL turn its extra sanitary water into greywater. Best of all, the product was created right in western Pennsylvania, just 60 miles away from Phipps.

Called the Epiphany Solar Water System, the product uses parabolic solar dishes lined with reflective coating to generate heat that powers multi-stage distillation units to create clean water. Originally designed to serve populations without direct or adequate access to clean drinking water, the Epiphany units can turn contaminated water into potable water using only the sun's energy.

The team agreed with Piacentini that the Epiphany units, which produce pharmaceutical-grade distilled water, would provide the ideal irrigation source for the Conservatory's delicate orchids, which do not respond well to the minerals found in the municipal supply. Now, six distilling units sit on the roof of the Production Greenhouses to serve such a purpose. (The team explored the possibility of keeping Epiphany units on the CSL site, but there was simply no room to accommodate them.)

On cloudy days when the units are not operating at full power, the excess effluent flows from the sanitary system to the two underground 12,000-gallon tanks adjacent to the restored Department of Public Works structures that had previously been used to store fuel. The tanks were tested for contaminants, thoroughly cleaned and transferred from the City of Pittsburgh to Phipps. They now serve as temporary holding tanks for water that awaits the next sunny day, when it travels through the Epiphany system and on to the Orchid Room.

115

A WATER-FRIENDLY LANDSCAPE

With the CSL water systems designed, it was important to determine which plant species and soil types would work best in the landscape while serving the water efficiency goal, enhancing the aesthetic impact of the site, and furthering its educational mission. In this regard, plants and soils requiring less irrigation would be more sustainable. Still, the chosen species needed to be visually appealing to help draw visitors in, which meant that there needed to be a balance between hearty and delicate options. The Andropogon Associates team opted for a blend of deciduous, evergreen and understory trees, along with a variety of shrubs, vines, perennials, grasses and seed mixes.

"When you're considering landscapes that require constant life support, you have to make sure you're getting more out of them than just sustaining them. At a place like Phipps, it has to look good so the visiting public will think they're beautiful and want to come back to see them again. The more they return, the more they learn. So that may trump the requirement of having plants that use less water if it helps serve the mission."

JOSÉ ALMIÑANA
Andropogon Associates

116

THE WATER-ENERGY CONNECTION

The CSL's engineers were not only asked to create water-efficient systems but they were also charged with creating water-efficient systems that were as energy-efficient as possible. Their overall solutions to the project's site-specific water needs might have looked quite different had they not needed to keep the water systems' energy draws so low. For example, blackwater could have been processed with technology that takes less land volume and more energy while delivering the same reusable water result. But to achieve the dual water and energy goals of the Living Building Challenge, systems needed to be more economical.

The only electric pumps not figured into the overall water balance are those used to move stormwater from the lower to the upper campus. Because the water is being repurposed for use beyond the CSL's boundaries, the power needed to deliver the necessary volume of water is exempt from the project's Challenge-specific net-zero energy calculation. The additional benefit of reusing the water for irrigation made enough sense for the International Living Future Institute to permit the extra energy usage required to power the larger pumps.

"One of the biggest hurdles had to do with getting local officials to approve various systems in the project. Waste water treatment is a good example. At first, they balked. But the more we explained the process, the more agreeable they became. They didn't end up approving everything we proposed, but eventually we came up with solutions everyone could live with."

RICHARD V. PIACENTINI
Phipps Conservatory and
Botanical Gardens

WORKING WITH THE CITY

Of all the Living Building Challenge Petals, water requires the greatest interaction with the municipality that would otherwise serve the project's utility needs. Various members of the CSL team interacted with the City of Pittsburgh and the Allegheny County Health Department to ensure that the project met local codes, as well as Challenge requirements.

Since the CSL's multi-tiered waste water treatment system had never been implemented on any

other project, there was no precedent with which the city or county inspectors could compare it. Instead, team members had to walk them through and familiarize them with the various processes as the project progressed, making design revisions along the way in order to satisfy code requirements. In this way, the CSL has helped inform municipal officials about alternative site-specific water treatment solutions that can help cut down on the wasteful "use-and-lose" processes that have been in place for so many years.

117

"The complexity of the stormwater management and onsite sanitary treatment systems became really clear as the project team worked together to finalize the scope and logic of the water systems controls. Thanks to the diversity of the team's expertise, many different scenarios — from emergency backups to net-zero energy — were identified and integrated into the final site water systems designs."

JASON WIRICK
Phipps Conservatory and Botanical Gardens

THE BEAUTY IN THE BIG PICTURE

The CSL is home to numerous innovative and sustainable water systems, both inside and outside of the building. However, it is the combination of these approaches that makes the project one of a kind from a water-efficiency standpoint.

While other buildings treat water using constructed wetlands and store stormwater on site, the CSL's design-engineering-construction team made individual solutions even better by tying them to one another. The result is a cohesive set of strategies that works most effectively when connected.

> "The original stormwater management plan for the CSL was to let all of the water infiltrate back into the ground. But the Living Building Challenge sort of compelled all of us to take our ideas for this project further. So when Phipps decided to capture and reuse the stormwater for the upper campus, we all figured out a way to make it happen."
>
> **FRED PAPE**
> Aquascape

BRILLIANCE RISES TO THE SURFACE

Designing the CSL's overall water strategy was one of the project's most complex and time-intensive aspects, which was further complicated by several major direction shifts along the way. Deciding to pump stormwater to Phipps' upper campus required a substantial set of design changes after construction had begun, as did deciding to send up to 200 gallons of water per day to the rooftop solar distilleries. While each change led to a potential performance improvement, it still required the team to stop, redesign and reconfigure before proceeding in the new direction.

Despite these challenges, the CSL's sophisticated water strategy will now benefit countless future projects and professionals by showing what is possible. Even if no other building incorporates the CSL's entire collection of solutions, elements of the overall approach may be used to achieve certain levels of water performance.

THE INDOOR QUALITY PETAL

Ensuring a Healthy Interior

121

SUMMARY OF THE LIVING BUILDING CHALLENGE VERSION 1.3 INDOOR QUALITY PETAL

Petal Intent

The intent of this Petal is not to address all of the potential ways that an interior environment could be compromised, but to focus on best practices to create a healthy interior environment.

Petal Imperatives

- A Civilized Environment
- Healthy Air: Source Control
- Healthy Air: Ventilation

122

INTERIORS THAT
HONOR THE OUTDOORS

The goal of the Indoor Quality Petal is to provide clean, civilized indoor environments for the majority of the population and the majority of building occupants. It is not intended to create sterile interiors suitable for individuals requiring extremely hygienic conditions. It seeks to redefine the notion of how healthy interiors look, feel and affect people, while encouraging a connection between the inside and the outside of a Living Building. Because a healthy space is a civilized space.

123

THE WINDOW DEBATE AT THE CENTER FOR SUSTAINABLE LANDSCAPES

The Center for Sustainable Landscapes' (CSL) design-build team devoted a significant amount of time to the topic of the building's windows. First, the architects ensured that every room had plenty of glazing to allow visual access to the outside. Second, they created a layout that guaranteed occupants close proximity to the building's perimeter to enhance the structure's indoor-outdoor character (and to meet Living Building Challenge requirements).

"We felt it was so important for people to understand what's going on outside. People should know whether it's hot, cold, humid, sunny or raining. They should be able to tune in to the season. People can't connect with nature in a place with all automated windows."

RICHARD V. PIACENTINI
Phipps Conservatory and Botanical Gardens

124

Then questions began to be raised about the windows' operations. How should they work in conjunction with the building's heating and cooling systems? Should they open and close automatically according to systems that tracked temperature and airflow, and triggered programmable actions? Or should they be manually operated by the building's occupants?

Initially, the team leaned toward allowing computers to control the windows, primarily because it seemed like an easy way to ensure efficiency. Automating operations would take the onus off of the busy occupants and help keep the building's performance numbers where they needed to be. And, ultimately, it would be a shame to delay Challenge certification simply because a few windows were left open after the heat or the air conditioning kicked on.

However, the more the team discussed the issue, the more they realized that having fully computer-controlled window operations would go against everything that the CSL and the Challenge sought to embrace: the human connection to nature. They agreed that computers should not bear sole responsibility for determining when to introduce fresh air into an interior space. There needed to be a human component to the decision-making process driven by people's individual senses of comfort, as well as their direct access to the elements.

So a hybrid system was developed. The upper CSL windows that are out of vertical reach are automatically controlled based on feedback from temperature and airflow sensors, while those that fall within reach of the occupants are all manually operated. This feature allows outdoor air to be drawn into the interior through open windows, where it mixes with the existing interior air and circulates efficiently throughout the space.

Before finalizing the plans, engineers ran computational fluid dynamics to test various temperature profiles inside and outside of the structure, ultimately determining that dual upper and lower window openings resulted in the best air circulation within the building. They also found that the CSL's narrow 40-foot space helps optimize air manipulation when upper and lower windows are open on both the north and south façades.

"There's an old saying: 'Passive buildings require active people, and vice versa.' So if you want passive systems, you need people willing to physically go and make the changes — turn things off, put up shading or whatever — versus automating everything to the point where people don't have to think about it."

MARCUS SHEFFER
7Group

Windows, including these at the top of the CSL's atrium, became a subject of debate among team members regarding the proper balance between human and mechanical controls.

COMFORT BY DEGREES

Pittsburgh's winter lows average in the 20s and summer highs average in the 80s to 90s, with high humidity conditions. Relying on passive solar and natural ventilation during spring and fall was one thing, but the CSL would require mechanical heating and cooling for the more extreme seasons. The use of natural ventilation instead of mechanical cooling calls for judgment on the part of the occupants in addition to automated systems. More specifically, the team needed natural ventilation functions to be driven by a combination of human and electronic controls.

So the team created a computerized system that automatically alerts key operations personnel when temperatures and humidity levels rise or fall out of the desired range in which natural ventilation might not be effective to keep the interior space comfortable. (The engineers established an initial comfort band ranging between 68 and 78 degrees Fahrenheit for the CSL's interior, which occupants will further adjust based on their experience in the building.)

When the system indicates that outdoor conditions are suitable for natural ventilation — via low humidity, appropriate temperature ranges and suitable outdoor air quality — the operations personnel can set the controls to open upper window sections and shut down the building's HVAC system. Personnel must also manually open lower window sections to create effective natural ventilation flow. When conditions fall outside of the suitable range for natural ventilation, the operations personnel initiate the control sequences to turn on the HVAC system and close the upper window sections. Occupants must close the lower window sections manually. Phipps Conservatory and Botanical Gardens personnel will gradually learn what indoor comfort conditions are suitable for the majority of the staff and the ranges of outdoor temperatures and humidity levels that can provide those conditions when opening the windows.

Overall, the CSL contains a three-stage cooling system to manage the interior air temperature and keep occupants comfortable. Within this system, users are educated about optimal times and conditions when they should manually open and close windows.

1. Upon arrival on a summer morning, for example, people might choose to open the building's exterior windows.

2. As temperature and humidity levels rise, the moisture in the air will automatically trigger an alert that the windows should be closed. A desiccant wheel will then be activated, removing the humidity from the interior and returning the drier air to a more comfortable state without the need for air conditioning.

3. Only in extreme high-temperature situations will the air conditioning system need to be turned on.

For more on the CSL's heating and cooling system, see the Energy Petal section beginning on page 64.

> *"The desiccant wheel takes the mugginess out of the air and returns cool, dry, comfortable air. Taking the moisture out of the air before it comes in contact with the AC system actually reduces the stress on the AC load. So it's doing a lot of things for us with very little energy impact."*
>
> **ALAN TRAUGOTT**
> CJL Engineering

A raised floor allows for an energy-efficient air distribution system.

DISPLACEMENT VENTILATION

The CSL's underfloor air distribution system requires very little energy while delivering the cleanest possible air to the building's occupants. Slow fans push cool filtered air through the sub-floor and then up through vents at floor level. Once the air reaches the room and begins to cool the area, its natural buoyancy carries it upward along with any unwanted CO_2 from exhalation and indoor pollutants. Finally, displacement removes this dirtier air from the breathing zone and sends it out via ceiling-mounted return air ducts. This approach is an improvement over typical energy-taxing systems, which drive air from above and push it through the spaces, mixing new air with the old.

128

AN OPEN FLOOR PLAN KEEPS EVERYTHING MOVING

The interior of the CSL is minimally partitioned to enhance daylight and maintain the highest possible ventilation quality. Most work spaces are open and modular, with dividers that are high enough off the ground to facilitate floor-level air circulation and low enough in height to allow good daylight penetration throughout the space. Additionally, many of the few walls that exist contain glass so that light can easily pass through them.

The open design and air flow systems even informed furniture choices. When the project team considered products for the space, members looked for tables and desks with sufficient vertical clearance from the floor (as opposed to solid side panels) that would allow the air to circulate in the most efficient manner possible.

The interior layout incorporates both public (viewable to visitors) and private (for administrative use) areas. Although the CSL houses the organization's administrative offices, it was also designed to fulfill an educational mission. The trick was to create office space that is separate and secure but still connected within the larger framework of the public portions of the building, where visitors are welcome. These two sections needed to be independent but work in conjunction with one another.

129

QUALITY IN, QUALITY THROUGHOUT

The CSL's engineers relied on the fact that the building's heating-ventilation-air-conditioning (HVAC) system could not create air quality; it could only maintain it. In order for the interior air to remain clean and healthy, the contents of the space had to be just as pure. The Living Building Challenge Materials Petal minimized the introduction of toxic supplies used to build, paint and carpet the structure. But the cleanliness of the contents of the spaces is up to the occupants to uphold.

Already, the air quality in the CSL is better than that of a typical office given the low-emitting materials used to construct the building. The less the fabrics, materials and desk accessories off-gas into the interior environment, the cleaner the air that circulates through the HVAC system.

Additionally, live plants are everywhere inside of the CSL, serving as aesthetically pleasing air-cleaning tools that further the horticultural message of Phipps and create a biophilic atmosphere. Besides the proposed green wall in the atrium space and the green roof on the building, plants line the tops of the cubicle dividers and appear on desktops. Even these are carefully oriented to be visible and inspirational, without interfering with light passing through the space.

"*You can avoid VOCs, maintain good housekeeping practices and use green cleaning supplies as a way of creating good indoor air quality without having to go all the way to the Living Building Challenge level. But the Challenge adds another, more stringent dimension that allows you to go further.*"

ALAN TRAUGOTT
CJL Engineering

131

THE
BEAUTY +
INSPIRATI
PETAL

Enriching the Experience

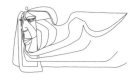

133

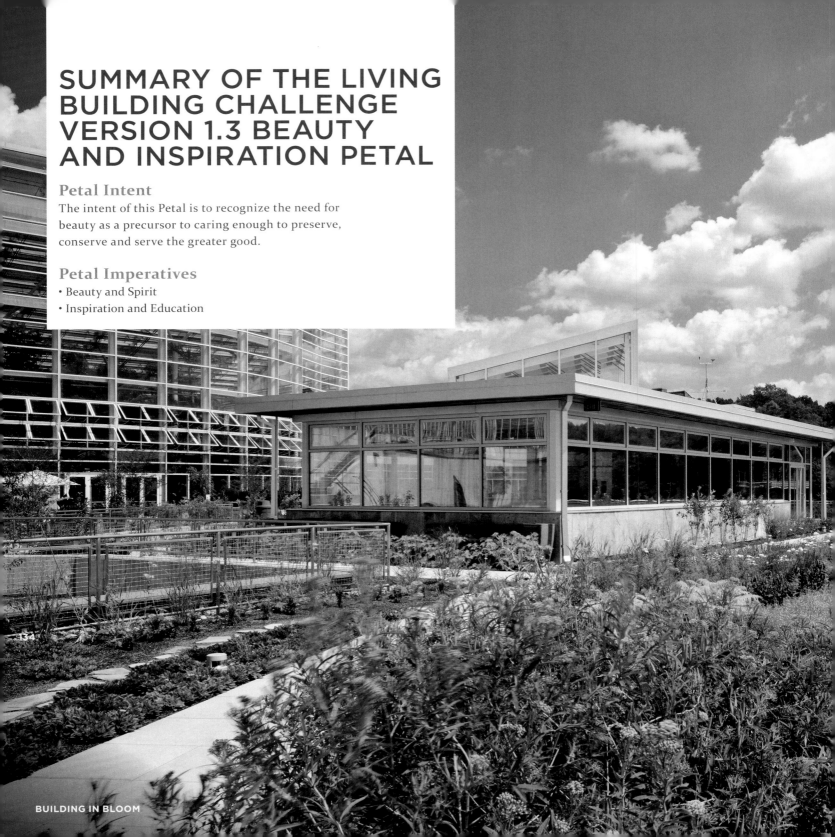

SUMMARY OF THE LIVING BUILDING CHALLENGE VERSION 1.3 BEAUTY AND INSPIRATION PETAL

Petal Intent

The intent of this Petal is to recognize the need for beauty as a precursor to caring enough to preserve, conserve and serve the greater good.

Petal Imperatives

• Beauty and Spirit
• Inspiration and Education

134

"We are all about beauty at Phipps, and it is very important to us that the Center for Sustainable Landscapes reflects the same values we highlight everywhere else in the Conservatory."

RICHARD V. PIACENTINI
Phipps Conservatory and
Botanical Gardens

AN INSPIRATIONAL JOURNEY THROUGH THE PROPERTY

The Center for Sustainable Landscapes (CSL) embodies this sixth and final Petal of version 1.3 of the Living Building Challenge. Its structure symbolizes beauty in the built environment; its purpose furthers an educational mission; its surroundings celebrate nature's inspiration. Most of all, the CSL demonstrates how sustainable design can be elegant and inviting.

135

EDUCATING THE VISITING PUBLIC

The paths leading people into and around the CSL are meant to be more than plain walkways. They are designed to offer a literal and figurative passage through the many innovations built into the property — from the back side of Phipps Conservatory and Botanical Gardens' upper campus all the way down the three floors of the CSL building, weaving in and out of the surrounding landscape.

While researching appropriate ways to welcome and lead visitors, the team asked several questions:

- Will it be disorienting for people to arrive at this building via its roof, which sits on the same plane as the ground floor of the upper campus?

- How should we take people down through the building's 25-foot drop in elevation?

- Is it possible to incorporate the cliff's steep grade into a site-wide inspirational journey?

- What landscape design will best echo the desired narrative for the building and its educational function?

- Are there solutions that will satisfy municipal safety code requirements without detracting from the beauty of the site?

- Can we continue to educate people at virtually every step of the way?

- How can we actively engage visitors in demonstrations of the building's performance efficiencies?

The answers were rich and diverse, yielding an assortment of solutions. Able-bodied visitors to the CSL may take direct routes between points, using staircases that become part of the amphitheater. Individuals with mobility issues may choose a gently sloping path that travels from the roof level down one story, where it enters the building's atrium on the second floor. On the ground level, visitors find just what they would at the bottom of a hill: pools of water alongside plants that thrive in wet soil.

This shifting, dynamic landscape inside and outside of the CSL helps people learn what happens in nature. Wherever people are on the site, they gain a better understanding of the natural systems that inform the building. Interpretive panels explain various operational systems within the structure and track real-time performance numbers for both energy and water. Sensors placed throughout the interior monitor the patterns of air flow and foot traffic so that heating, cooling and ventilation systems may be adjusted for maximum efficiency. Their data are visible to visitors, too, via a touchscreen panel in the atrium.

136

"A growing body of research across many disciplines, aligned with a wide array of anecdotal evidence, suggests that contact with nature and its beauty can improve people's psychological well-being, intellectual abilities and creativity. This building benefits people by connecting them to nature."

MOLLY STEINWALD
Phipps Conservatory and Botanical Gardens

Phipps' Director of Science Education and Research Molly Steinwald (seated, far right) and High School Program Coordinator Kate Borger (standing, far right) pose with student interns from the Fairchild Challenge Program that connects students with art and nature.

"In many ways, we now have a counterpart to what happens in the Conservatory. There, we bring nature inside the glass and something inspiring happens, creating an extraordinary opportunity for learning. It's a very interesting comparison to the education that takes place in the CSL."

JOSÉ ALMIÑANA
Andropogon Associaties

Delegates from the One Young World 2012 conference were among the first people to gather in the CSL's classroom spaces. They came from around the globe to participate in workshops in which they exchanged ideas and explored solutions related to sustainability in all regions of the planet.

Interpretive panels explain the Living Building Challenge petal intents to CSL visitors and occupants.

"Phipps used to have classes in traditional lecture rooms that were disconnected from the greenhouse and the outdoors. In the CSL, instead of looking at pictures of outdoor spaces, you're directly linked to them. There's an excitement about these classes at Phipps, partly because these young students get to be in spaces that are so exciting."

VIVIAN LOFTNESS
Carnegie Mellon University School of Architecture

EDUCATING STUDENTS

Well before Richard V. Piacentini and his colleagues re-envisioned the CSL as a Living Building, they knew that they wanted it to house the bulk of Phipps' educational programs for children. Previously, a number of the organization's educational events for youth, adults and seniors took place at various locations around the upper campus and at Phipps Garden Center in the Shadyside district of Pittsburgh. Now, many of these programs incorporate the CSL and its landscape, and refer to the many interpretive materials distributed throughout the site. Many of the children's programs are held in the lower level of the CSL in a profoundly experiential indoor/outdoor classroom where instructors balance visual and tactile curriculum.

In fact, for many children's and school programs, buses drop students at the lower campus and educational instruction begins at the ground floor of the CSL. From there, tours continue through the building's three levels, pass by interpretive displays about its operational functions, lead into the Conservatory and the rest of the upper campus, and then end at the Welcome Center.

EDUCATING THE PROFESSIONS

The educational impact of the Living Building Challenge is not limited to the general public. It is also designed to broaden the perspectives of architects, engineers, builders and manufacturers. In this regard, the CSL has been a wildly successful endeavor.

Being among the first to register for the Challenge, the CSL team did not have the luxury of referring to case studies or documentation from previous projects. So team members were on their own to design and construct a structure with virtually no precedent. Proven operational systems could be incorporated into the master plan, but the start-to-finish process of creating the CSL according to the Imperatives of the Challenge put the team to the test.

On the job site, the Turner Construction crew had to ensure that every contractor, vendor, manufacturer and offsite contractor was willing to cooperate with the project's objectives. In fact, before any new personnel came onto the site, Turner had these individuals attend a modified orientation meeting. Along with standard safety curriculum, this CSL-specific session offered a "sustainability orientation." It covered the basic goals of the job and the ways in which each new hire could contribute to the project's success. This approach helped educate the professionals contributing their skills to the building, while also creating a group of potential advocates who could then take their new knowledge back out into the field.

Since no harmful chemicals were used to build the CSL, it offers a clean, healthy space for staff, visitors and students of all ages.

"The CSL will absolutely enhance the productivity of its inhabitants, since a part of productivity is one's general motivation. This building will be a light, airy, daylit, brilliant space with wonderful vistas. It will be a delightful place to work."

VIVIAN LOFTNESS
Carnegie Mellon University
School of Architecture

EDUCATING OCCUPANTS

It could be said that the people who regularly inhabit the CSL will be the ones who are most profoundly influenced by it. Phipps employees who report daily to the structure are surrounded by nature, while working to promote its value to others.

For many staff members, the move to the CSL signified a dramatic shift, as they went from working in separate mobile offices to working side by side. In this way, the open layout of the CSL's interior does more than just maximize energy and light efficiencies; it also ushers in the opportunity for colleagues to engage more meaningfully with one another as they go about their business. The building itself, then, may be thought of as yet another contributing member of the Phipps collaborative.

141

142

THE BEAUTY-INSPIRATION CONNECTION

The CSL stands not just as a green building showcase, but also as an elegant organic classroom that teaches all who pass through and around it.

This accomplishment begins with the landscaping, which serves multiple purposes: to meet human beings' biophilic needs with its lush and live surroundings, to enhance the building's performance, and to educate people about how those surroundings contribute to the health of the site. The landscape's greenery — an important component of the didactic missions of both the CSL and Phipps at large — performs aesthetic and practical functions, and continues to evolve over time. As it changes, it introduces new opportunities to study how species adapt to fluctuating environmental circumstances. At each step, the landscape inspires anew.

The same must be said for the physical structure at the heart of this groundbreaking project. The fact that a human construction is capable of eliciting an emotional response speaks to the inherent beauty of the CSL. Whether moved by its dramatic salvaged wood siding, awed by its generous glazing, or simply struck by the juxtaposition of its repurposed materials and its high-tech systems, one cannot help but marvel at the CSL's aesthetic impact. This one structure shows what we are capable of creating in our built environment, now and always: performance and sustainability, delightfully expressed.

Man-made designs inspired by nature
are abundant in and around the CSL.

144

BUILDING IN BLOOM

Sustainable Landscapes

"When we think about the type of world we would want our children and grandchildren to inherit, it is easy to see why the Living Building Challenge is so important. And when we look at how a dedicated team of professionals came together to create the CSL, we know that we have the technology and capacity to create that future now."

RICHARD V. PIACENTINI
Phipps Conservatory and Botanical Gardens

145

The Beauty & Inspiration Petal: **ENRICHING THE EXPERIENCE**

INTERNATIONAL
LIVING FUTURE INSTITUTE

The International Living Future Institute is an environmental NGO
committed to catalyzing the transformation toward communities
that are socially just, culturally rich and ecologically restorative. The
Institute is premised on the belief that providing a compelling vision
for the future is a fundamental requirement for reconciling humanity's
relationship with the natural world. The Institute operates the Living
Building Challenge, the built environment's most rigorous performance
standard, and Declare, an ingredients label for building materials. It
houses the Cascadia Green Building Council and Ecotone Publishing.

ECOTONE PUBLISHING

Founded by green building experts in 2004, Ecotone Publishing is
dedicated to meeting the growing demand for authoritative and
accessible books on sustainable design, materials selection and
building techniques in North America and beyond. Located in the
Cascadia region, Ecotone is well positioned to play an important part
in the green design movement. Ecotone searches out and documents
inspiring projects, visionary people and vital trends that are leading the
design industry to transformational change toward a healthier planet.

LIVING BUILDING CHALLENGE

The Living Building Challenge is the built environment's most
rigorous performance standard. It calls for the creation of
building projects at all scales that operate as cleanly, beautifully
and efficiently as nature's architecture. To be certified under the
Challenge, projects must meet a series of ambitious performance
requirements, including net-zero energy, waste and water,
over a minimum of 12 months of continuous occupancy.

LIVING BUILDING PARTNERS

Phipps is extremely grateful for the support of our staff, board, volunteers and lead donors — Richard King Mellon Foundation, The Heinz Endowments, Athena Sarris and Colcom Foundation — who, with hundreds of other generous contributors, have made this singular advancement possible for Phipps, our region and our planet. We also would like to thank the International Living Future Institute for presenting us with this challenge, and for their support throughout the process.

ORGANIZATIONS

Carnegie Mellon University — Center for Building Performance and Diagnostics

Cascadia Green Building Council

Chatham University

Duquesne University

Green Building Alliance

International Living Future Institute℠

National Energy Technology Laboratory

Pennsylvania Department of Economic Development

Pennsylvania Department of Environmental Protection

The Sustainable Sites Initiative™

University of Pittsburgh — Mascaro Center for Sustainable Innovation

U.S. Department of Energy

PITTSBURGH AND PENNSYLVANIA BASED DESIGN TEAM

The Design Alliance Architects; Architecture, Pittsburgh

Andropogon Associates; Landscape Architecture, Philadelphia

Atlantic Engineering Services; Structural Engineering, Pittsburgh

Civil & Environmental Consultants; Civil Engineering and Water Engineering, Pittsburgh

CJL Engineering; MEP Engineering, Pittsburgh

evolveEA; LEED® and Living Building Challenge Management, Pittsburgh

H.F. Lenz; Commissioning, Johnstown

Kolano Design; Interpretation, Pittsburgh

Massaro Corporation; Pre-Construction Management, Pittsburgh

Pitchford Diversified; Enhanced Commissioning, Butler

7group, LLC; Energy, Daylight and Materials Consultants, Kutztown

Sundrive; Water Treatment, Ottsville

GENERAL CONTRACTOR

Turner Construction; Pittsburgh

SUB-CONTRACTORS

Allegheny Installations; Allied Waste; Aquascape; Automated Logic; Berner International Corp.; Brayman Construction; Tom Brown Contracting; Burns and Scalo; Compu-Site; Continental Building Systems; S.A. Comunale; Definis Mechanical Contractors; D-M Products; Dubin and Company; Energy Independent Solutions; Engineered Products; Epiphany Solar Water Systems; A. Folino Construction; Franco; Franklin Interiors; Giffin Interior & Fixture; Glass House Renovation Services; Hanlon Electric; Ionadi Corporation; Lutron Electronics; Marshall Elevator; Massaro Industries; Mats Inc.; A.G. Mauro; Mele Landscaping Contractors; Mendel Steel; Noralco Corporation; Montgomery Smith Inc.; TD Patrinos Painting & Contracting; PPG Industries; Saints Painting; J.C. Schultz Interiors; SSM Industries; Spectra Contract Flooring; Tri-State Lockers & Shelving; Western Pennsylvania Geothermal Heating and Cooling

OTHER CONSULTANTS

Indevco; Owner's Representative, Pittsburgh

Vermeulens Cost Consultants; Estimating, Toronto

PHOTO AND DIAGRAM CREDITS

All photos by Denmarsh Photography, Inc. except as noted:

Ed Rombout Photography: page 3

Jonathan Payne: page 5

Courtesy of Phipps Conservatory Archives: pages 8, left;
9, top left; 10, top right, top left, bottom left; 11

Courtesy of Carnegie Library Archives: pages 8, right;
9, top right, bottom left, bottom right; 10, bottom right

Renee Rosensteel: pages 16; 59, top right;
80; 82; 97, right; 125, top; 138

Andropogon Associates, Ltd.: pages 22-23, 26-27, 30-31, 34-35, 60-61

Joshua Franzos: pages 24-25, 28-29, 33

Randie Snow: pages 30, 63

The Design Alliance Architects: pages 32, 38-43, 84-87, 110-113

Joe Cooper-Silvis, The Think Tank Group, Inc.: page 36

KD Reilly: pages 44-45

Paul g. Wiegman: pages 50-51; 58, left; 62; 74; 76; 78-79;
96, right; 97, left; 115; 130-133; 145, top left, bottom left

Elaine Kramer: page 52-53

Hawkeye Aerial Photography: page 54

Nicholas Hartkopf: 72

QA Graphics: page 83

softfirm: page 101

Julia Petruska: page 137